MOON WITHOUT STARS

Jill found her life serene on the South
African farm owned by her brother and his
wife – until the advent of the superior Dean
Lester, a timber planter, who had taken over
Nyala Mount, a neighbouring property. It
took the arrival of the glamorous Sylvia
de Courcy to make Jill realize she didn't
dislike Dean any more . . .

MOON WITHOUT STARS

by

ANNE HAMPSON

MILLS & BOON LIMITED
17-19 FOLEY STREET
LONDON W1A 1DR

First Published 1974
This edition 1974

© Anne Hampson 1974

ISBN 0 263 71594 9

Made and Printed in Great Britain by
Cox & Wyman Ltd, London, Reading
and Fakenham

CHAPTER ONE

THE day's work was done, and although affected both in mind and body by that state of tiredness that follows healthy hard work, Jill climbed the kopje to enjoy the African sunset.

So much colour! Was ever anything more breathtaking and dramatic? Already cut in half by the distant purple horizon, the great crimson ball was fast sinking in a final blaze of glory. While she watched, the fire and flame melted into a cloud of amber and within minutes it was a mere blush of rose that spread across the silent bushveld.

Allowing her interest to wander, Jill gazed at her brother's homestead, peeping through the willow trees, down there in the valley of the Batuwa River. Tin-roofed with whitewashed walls, it was unprepossessing from the outside, while within it was a comfortable and well-loved home, the home to which her brother and his wife had brought her after the tragic death of her father in a road accident.

Movement caught her attention; the native boys leaving the maize and soya fields and strolling towards the kraal where their wives and piccanins awaited them.

Her attention returned to the sunset; she watched the radiant tapestry of rose and peach take on a purple hue that formed a gentle arc against the pearl of the evening sky.

Silence reigned over the drowsy bushveld; she turned

her head, scarcely aware of the action, and her eyes found the great expanse of forest trees which lay nodding among the mauve and indigo shadows that were all that remained of the transient afterglow of sunset. A white-gabled, blue-shuttered colonial mansion lay to the left of those trees, a luxurious homestead with an upper storey and a pillared vine-shaded stoep running the whole length of the imposing front. And there was a similar stoep at the back. Dome palms graced both sides of the drive; the gardens, lavishly laid out with trees and shrubs and every kind of exotic flower imaginable, were a paradise of good taste.

Jill uttered a small sigh of regret. How very pleasant it had been when the Fenwicks lived there! – the Fenwicks who were always so friendly and eager for visitors, who could proffer help without being so arrogantly aware of their superior knowledge all the time. Not so with Dean Lester who, three months ago, had purchased Nyala Mount when, on the advice of his doctor, Mr. Fenwick had decided to retire from the active life necessary in the growing of timber.

A frown creased Jill's high wide forehead as she continued to stare, unable to see the homestead as it was too far away – half a mile away, along the road to Breysburg, the nearest town, which was fourteen miles from Bangali Farm, the home of Bob and Lucie, Jill's brother and sister-in-law. The frown was caused by the vision of Dean Lester ... haughty, high-handed, oozing self-assurance and obsessed by a sense of his own superiority. Sarcastic, cynical, disdainful of women, he was just about as insufferable as any man could be.

Retracing her steps at last, Jill joined her brother on

6

the stoep. Relaxing after a hard day's work, he was leaning back luxuriously in his cane chair and drawing contentedly on his pipe.

'Had a nice walk?' Bob automatically pulled forth a chair and Jill sat down.

'I went to the top of the kopje to see the sunset.'

Her brother smiled.

'You can see it very well from here.'

Jill laughed and nodded in agreement.

'But you always feel you gain a better view of anything if you have to climb for it.' Bob merely drew on his pipe again and she continued, 'The colours – this lovely country is full of them, so full that they take your breath away.'

'You haven't yet become used to the beauty?' It was almost twelve months since that day when, having flown to England for the funeral, Bob and his wife had brought Jill back with them after seeing to all the details of selling up the home and other necessary tasks which Jill in her grief was quite unable to do for herself.

She and her father had lived alone for five years – ever since Bob, having met and married a South African girl, had decided to settle in her country. Between them he and Lucie had managed to buy Bangali Farm, which had taken all their savings, and in consequence they were still struggling to get on their feet. Jill and her father had enjoyed a comradely relationship, both working in the same office and, when at home, sharing such things as shopping, gardening and household chores. So it was natural that Jill should be devastated by his untimely death, and owing to this she had made no demur when her future had been quietly and efficiently arranged for her by Bob and Lucie. Like one hypnotized she had allowed herself to be led, yet with the vague idea at the back of her mind that she would probably come to regret her easy acquiescence once time had eclipsed the initial pangs of pain and shock. However, it transpired that regret was never for one single moment to assail her. She was as content – in a different kind of way – as when living with her father. Right from the first Lucie and Bob had been wonderfully understanding, never even commenting if she should suddenly leave some task she was doing and wander off into the silence and peace of the veld. This she would often do in the beginning when sadness held her firmly in its grip. Right in the middle of some gardening task, or looking to the poultry, or even cooking, she would suddenly have to get away, all by herself, to dwell on the past when she was mistress of her own home, doing just what she liked in it – and with it also, for she was always painting or decorating or fitting some modern addition to the kitchen or bathroom. She liked moving the furniture around, enjoyed changing the ornaments from one room to another.

On her return from these wanderings Jill would look from her brother to his wife, overwhelmed by pangs of guilt. They would merely smile at her and inform her that the meal was ready, or mention that one of the Fenwicks had called to invite the three of them over for a sundowner that evening. Yes, they had been so wonderfully understanding, and owing to this, and also to their deep sense of sympathy, Jill's recovery had progressed far more quickly than would otherwise have been possible.

8

Gradually she had been led into the social life of Breysburg, joining the club and attending the dances and other functions to which most of their far-flung neighbours would come. She went along with her brother and his wife whenever one of these neighbours gave a dinner-party or barbecue, and she had made a few friends in consequence. She had got to know Patrick Mason, son of the owner of Wyburnfold, a property similar to that of Bob's, and run on the same lines with mixed farming predominating. Not that there was anything serious between Jill and Patrick; they were good friends, that was all, and both treated with amused disdain the rumours which naturally had resulted from their being seen together in town. These meetings occurred if Jill should happen to be doing some shopping for Lucie or Bob; she would let Patrick know she was going to town and if he could get away he would meet her. They would lunch together; he would later carry her parcels back to the station wagon. Heads would nod and tongues wag and Patrick would grin ruefully and say,

'What's the betting – they've got us engaged already?'

A small cough brought Jill back gently from her reflections and she threw her brother an affectionate smile.

'I'm sorry. I was lost in thought.' She knew that Bob would accept this, making no attempt to probe further. He was like that and so was Lucie. They waited for confidences, interested when interest was required but incurious once they saw that Jill preferred to remain uncommunicative about anything. 'You were remarking

9

that I hadn't got used to it here—' She shook her head. 'I hope it will never become so familiar that I fail to appreciate its beauty.'

'I'm glad you've taken to our place, Jill.' Bob's grey eyes were serious as they met hers. 'Both Lucie and I have had qualms at times, wondering whether we did right. We didn't realize at the time that we were in effect badgering you into coming here.'

'No such thing,' protested Jill. 'I made my own choice.'

The shade of a smile appeared at that and he said,

'It's generous of you, but it's not the truth. You didn't know what you were doing and it's mainly good luck that things have turned out satisfactorily. We were greatly troubled at one time – when you seemed so unsettled – about our having persuaded you to sell your little place. It would have been pretty grim had you not adapted to the change and been forced to return to England with no home to go to.'

'Well, I have adapted, and it'll take a good deal to move me.' Her voice took on the huskiness that invariably crept into it on those occasions when emotion was strong, be it happy emotion or sad. 'Thank you for having me, Bob,' she ended simply, and a frown instantly settled on his fair, handsome features.

'Can we have an end, once and for all, to the gratitude?' he said, still frowning. 'What was more natural than that Lucie and I should wish you to share our home when Father died? And look at the help you give us – cleaning and cooking in the house, looking to the poultry outside, as well as driving the tractor when necessary.'

'I enjoy it all, especially driving the tractor. It's so marvellous out there, under the sun, driving leisurely back and forth, with no traffic to get in my way and no one to bother if I decide I've had enough and leave the work for a while.'

'You like being your own boss as it were?' He nodded thoughtfully. 'So do I. It's good, as you say, to be able to down tools for a space and go off and do something else.'

'The work's so rewarding,' she said dreamily, her eyes moving towards the field she had been harrowing earlier in the day. 'I love to look at what I've done, especially when I've been clearing ground of weeds and other rubbish.' She gave a happy laugh. 'I shall never go back to an office. If you and Lucie ever throw me out I'll go and find a job on another farm.'

'Throw you out? That's not likely and you know it.'

'I was thinking the other day, if you decide to raise a family . . .?'

'There'll still be room for you. We can always build on.'

'Yes, that's possible.' Jill's gaze returned to her brother. She often wished he and Lucie would go in for children; she would delight in being an aunt. Jill had mentioned this to Lucie one day, in a light vein, of course, and her sister-in-law's response had been,

'Why don't you get married and have some of your own seeing that you're so fond of them?'

But there never had been any thought of marriage in Jill's mind. She had not yet met the kind of man with whom she could visualize living out the rest of her days.

She was far too choosey, her father used to say when after two or three dates with a boy she would refuse to see him again. It were far better to be choosey than to make a mistake, decided Jill, and now at twenty-four she was almost resigned to spinsterhood, since it was most unlikely she would meet her ideal out here in these wilds. And as she had just said, she would never leave the farm – not of her own accord.

'You're dreaming again.' Bob's voice interrupted her thoughts, cutting through the whirring of cicadas and other familiar sounds coming from the garden.

'I must go and have a bath. You're not wanting the bathroom for a few minutes?'

Bob shook his head.

'No, Jill; carry on.' He watched her rise, his eyes travelling over her slender figure and noting the dusty trews and soiled shirt, the broad-brimmed hat pushed right back to reveal the sun-bleached hair framing the high forehead and blue-veined temples. The natural colour of her hair was light brown and since coming out to the Transvaal she had worn it quite short, elfin-style, flicking up at the ends and with a half fringe that also flicked up at the ends so that no matter how much trouble she might take her hair never appeared in that state which could be described as immaculate. Her cheekbones were high, her skin clear and golden, her eyes a soft brown, large and trusting, like those of a faithful dog, her father had often teasingly said.

'I'll not be long – ten minutes or so,' promised Jill as she moved towards the open french window.

'You needn't rush,' he frowned. 'Give yourself a little longer than that. You'll need to soak in order to get the tiredness out of your bones,' he added, and Jill laughed.

'My bones aren't aching, thank you very much! I'm not bent with the rheumatics yet.'

Her brother responded to her mood and for a few moments there was a little lively exchange of words between the two. Hearing it, Lucie appeared, her pretty face flushed, a ridiculous wisp of an apron tied daintily around her waist. Fair, with blue eyes and a wide generous mouth, she had captivated her future father-in-law on her very first meeting with him.

'What are you two doing?' she demanded with mock severity. 'Can't you occupy yourselves more profitably? Have you no thought for the poor drudge who's sweating over a hot stove preparing your dinner? Bob, you can just come inside and get the table ready!'

'I'm going!' Jill dodged past her sister-in-law and hurried along to the bathroom.

How very enjoyable life was, she thought as she lay soaking for a luxurious few minutes. So much to do that one's mind was constantly occupied. Pleasant company, a night out now and then to add variety, a trip into town to shop whenever the necessity arose. She thought of Patrick, smiling faintly to herself. He was young for his twenty-five years, and he was cheerful, which suited her since she would have been wary had he been of a more serious disposition. He lived on the surface of life, discovering something highly amusing in occasions and incidents which left others straight-faced; he laughed a lot, and by now Jill had discovered that to him life was just one long gay round of fun.

Against her will Jill was forced to allow another image

to intrude into her vision – that of Dean Lester, timber man with several other plantations scattered about this region of the northern Transvaal. She had met him at the Springbok Club in Breysburg, her brother having introduced her. He had met the man about a week after his arrival at Nyala Mount, when Dean condescended to call at Bangali Farm. Jill had been in the dairy and so had missed him, but both Bob and Lucie had, so they said, taken an instant liking to him.

'He's superior, but charming nevertheless,' from Lucie. 'A good-looker if ever I saw one!'

Ignoring that, Bob had said,

'Very knowledgeable. He's promised any help we might need. I think that once we get to know him he'll be a most acceptable neighbour.'

And so it was with a sort of mildly pleasant feeling of anticipation that Jill had got herself ready for the dance to be held at the club. She wore a long gown of wild silk – a sale bargain come by just before her father's death and worn on only one previous occasion. It looked – according to Lucie – worth a million dollars.

'Don't you feel right on top of the world in it?' she asked as Jill stood before the mirror in her bedroom.

'Yes, as a matter of fact I do,' admitted Jill, sparingly allowing herself a spray of perfume. 'But I do wish my hair would behave!'

'It's nice like that; gives you an urchin look and takes five years off your age.'

Jill turned.

'How much do you want to borrow?' and before Lucie could reply, 'You'll be unlucky. I went mad in town today, what with these silver shoes and my new undies and my hair-do – which was a sheer waste of money – and those necessities like talcum powder and toothpaste. I haven't a bean until the week-end.'

'Are you two girls ready?' Bob had called impatiently at last, and less than an hour later he was introducing her to their new neighbour.

Jill's pleasant feeling had subsided at once; never in her life could she recall taking an instant dislike to anyone, but she certainly took an instant dislike to Dean Lester. She disliked his manner and his arrogant bearing; she disliked his piercing, deep-set grey eyes because they seemed to see more than they should when looking her over. His handshake she resented because her fingers were crushed – quite unnecessarily, she thought, since the man must surely be aware of his own strength. His lips struck her as giving evidence of a sensuous nature; his taut jawline denoted implacability and she decided that when he married – if any woman were ever foolish enough to have him – he would rule his wife with a rod of iron.

His manner as they danced was uncommunicative and Jill felt he had little time for women in general. The odd one now and then might afford him a transient diversion, she supposed, but she could not by any stretch of imagination visualize his falling in love. She was irritated by the impression that he danced with her merely from a sense of duty and that he would rather be chatting with the men at the bar. But she was a neighbour and as such she must be treated to a certain amount of courtesy: that was the reason he danced with her several times during the evening. Jill found herself wishing Patrick had not been away on holiday. It would have been most satisfying to tell the pompous Dean Lester that she was booked for almost every dance.

She later found herself next to him at the buffet table; she was walking idly along with her plate, taking no interest in the food because she was not hungry. After walking the full length of the table without choosing anything she twisted about and began again.

'What's wrong? Nothing to suit your taste?'

Jill looked up into the face of Dean Lester – a handsome face, she grudgingly owned as her eyes took in the angular features, bronzed and finely-chiselled, the prominent cheekbones, gleaming through the clear taut skin, the trace of an amused smile that hovered on his lips. His grey eyes reflected this amusement but there was also a quality of cynicism in his expression which to some extent lessened its attractiveness.

'I wasn't thinking of food,' she replied with cool courtesy. 'My mind was on other things.'

'It was?' His long lean body seemed far too close and she stepped back. 'What things?' His deep-toned accents were clear and quiet, with that fine timbre that denotes high breeding. Jill found herself admitting that she could have admired that voice had her dislike of the man himself been less strong.

Surprised by his question, she shrugged her shoulders and answered a trifle impatiently,

'There was nothing of importance,' and she gave her attention to the food, helping herself to savouries. And as she did so it was suddenly borne in upon her that she had actually snubbed Dean Lester by her off-hand treatment of him. Bob and Lucie liked him enormously, being convinced of his proving to be a good neighbour.

And in view of this she, Jill, ought not to antagonize him. When presently she glanced up into his face it was to see a tight mouth and eyes glinting with a light she disliked exceedingly. His superiority was in evidence and she felt small and inadequate – and angry in consequence. Why couldn't he be *normal*, instead of acting like a king, or some equally exalted personage!

Within seconds of her snubbing him Jill found herself alone; Dean had taken what he wanted and gone. She bit her lip in vexation at her act, and the rest of her evening was spoiled by anxiety, since she feared he would keep away from Bangali Farm, a circumstance that would naturally lead to speculation on the part of Lucie and Bob and, because she was honest and frank, Jill knew she would have to confess to having antagonized him. This would upset her brother and sister-in-law, and although they would refrain from saying anything to her directly they must inevitably discuss the matter in her absence.

However, there was nothing she could do, and to her relief Dean did not after all keep away from the farm. In fact, he called a few days later to offer some saplings he had to spare, he also gave Bob some fruit trees with which to fill the spaces in the orchard. Left to herself, Jill would without hesitation have refused these gifts, but her brother received them gratefully, profuse in his thanks. On that particular visit Dean had extended to Jill the merest of glances and on leaving he nodded in her direction without speaking a word. He had invited them all over to Nyala Mount for a sundowner, and although Jill would have preferred to stay at home she could think of no excuse for doing so. And once again she had been treated with near indifference by her host.

This was how it had continued ever since – with each treating the other with stiff civility and nothing more. By some miracle they were able to do this without either Bob or Lucie even noticing the animosity that existed between them.

'Jill, I didn't say you could go to sleep in there!' Her brother's voice brought Jill back with a start and she hastily got out of the bath.

'Sorry,' she smiled on passing his bedroom on her way to her own. 'I was daydreaming again.'

'If I didn't know it was impossible, I'd swear you were in love!'

She merely laughed and passed on, relieved that Bob was not coupling her name with that of Patrick Mason.

Right from the start Bob had insisted that once a week Lucie and Jill each had a free day; it was Jill's the following day and after breakfast she set out to ride along the river bank. She took a packed lunch just in case she decided to laze away a few hours in some enchanted spot she might unexpectedly discover. It was one of the most attractive things about the place, she told herself many times, that surprises were always around the corner. Already she had found several delightful spots, and whenever she had time off she would make for one or other of them. However, today was to be one of further exploration, and she sang softly to herself as she jogged along on Jacky, the gelding which Bob had bought for his wife on her twenty-eighth birthday just over a year ago.

The sun was already hot as it rose slowly towards the almost vertical position it would occupy at noon; a haze touched the mountain crests and the sky was a shimmering canopy of deep metallic blue. Jill sighed contentedly and spurred her horse a little. Bob's boys were hard at work in the fields, Dick Reynolds the foreman watching them and Bob himself moving about among them. Both men waved as Jill rode along the edge of the field bordering the river, and she waved gaily back. Life was good, she thought, aware as ever of her good fortune in having a brother and sister-in-law who were so kind and understanding, and who had not hesitated to offer her a home at that most critical period in her life.

The men in the fields became lost to view and Jill experienced the exhilarating feeling of having the whole world to herself. Across the river the forest appeared dark; it moved like a stormy sea as the breeze filtered through the trees, swaying the branches and fluttering the leaves. Away to the west lay a great expanse of open veld, blue-green and indigo, grey and brown according as to how the breeze struck the vegetation, or to the effect of shadows cast by undulations and the low stony kopjes that lay scattered about the landscape. Flowers bloomed along the river, some like flames against the forest backcloth, some dangling, pendulous, towards the water; orchids, peach-pink or striped, purple-headed thistles, bell-flowers and gladioli ... So much colour, thought Jill, her eyes free to take it all in, her mind conditioned to the appreciation of the wonders lavishly arrayed by nature, her senses stimulated by the vista of sheer undiluted beauty. She rode along without a thought to time, her solitude complete.

At length she dismounted and sat down, having found a delightful loop in the river around which the tangled vegetation grew so thickly that it took on the aspect of a miniature jungle. Trees rose to a great height, their trunks supporting creepers which struggled for the light; birds with bright plumage flitted about, making happy noises which would be replaced now and then by the more guttural cry of a monkey as it swung agilely from branch to branch. Taking out her flask, Jill filled the cup with hot delicious coffee and was contentedly sipping it when the sound of hooves shattered the silence and resentment brought an instant frown to her brow. She looked up; there on the opposite bank was Dean Lester. Dismounting, he stood for a space watching her, that arrogant countenance seeming to be totally out of place among the simplicities of nature. With her customary manner of cool courtesy she called across the water,

'Good morning, Mr. Lester.'

'Good morning to you, Miss Sharman. Your day off, I presume?' He was tethering his horse to a tree and her frown deepened. She had no wish to carry on a conversation which necessitated raising her voice. But the man was already moving towards the narrow neck of the loop and she watched, fascinated, as with the most incredible leap he reached her side of the river. He said on noting her expression, 'Am I mistaken, or were you hoping I would land in the water?'

Colour surged into her cheeks; she was certainly put out of countenance by this uncanny interpretation of her thoughts. She had scarcely known herself of any conscious wish that he would fail to make the leap successfully. An unconscious hope that he would fail ... yes, most certainly she owned to the lurking of a sort of spiteful satisfaction at the idea of his making an undignified landing in the middle of the stream. Instead, he had accomplished the daring leap with the utmost ease and grace – hateful, *clever* creature that he was! And it was she herself who suffered embarrassment.

'Why should I harbour so uncharitable a wish as that?' she retorted, lifting her head in a gesture of indignation which served only to ignite a gleam of mockery in those deep-set grey eyes which at all times were so maddeningly disconcerting.

His response came after a pause during which he flicked her with his amused glance.

'Can you truthfully say you'd have been sorry to see me miss my footing? Or perhaps you'd have derived more satisfaction still if I had miscalculated the distance and never even come anywhere near to the bank?' Her heightened colour spread to her neck and his amusement grew. 'For your information, Miss Sharman, I can manage an additional foot and a half—' He thumbed downstream. 'There's another loop just along, which I negotiate regularly. It's eighteen inches wider than this.'

'It is?' with acid sweetness, 'and you troubled to measure it?'

'No, one of my boys did, just for his own amusement.' Dean glance at the space across from where she was seated. 'Any objections to my presence?' sarcastically and with a negligent flick of his hand, indicating the spot. 'I thought of sitting down.'

Jill's small pointed chin lifted. She felt the breeze on her face and hoped it would cool her off.

'I don't own the place,' she said.

'I'm perfectly aware of that.' He settled himself in comfort against the trunk of the mahogany tree and eyed her across the distance separating them.

'Perfectly aware . . .' Tingles ran vexatiously along her spine. 'It belongs to you?'

'Sorry,' he owned, the gleam of mocking satire returning to his eyes, 'but I'm afraid it does.'

'I didn't know,' she murmured on a distinctly pettish note.

'If you had you wouldn't be here.' A statement, and now the amusement was no longer present in his eyes. On the contrary, they had acquired a steely glint that had the effect of darkening their colour. 'Tell me,' he commanded in level, ice-edged tones, 'just what is it you don't like about me?'

She gave a start, such outspokenness being the last thing she would have expected. What must she say to him? How inordinately satisfying it would be to inform him that in her opinion he was a pompous, arrogant and insufferable man, that his pride irritated her and his air of superiority made her blood boil. But instead she adopted the tactful approach and, assuming an air of surprise, she said she had no idea how he had reached a conclusion like that. In response he made an abrupt movement which clearly portrayed suppressed impatience, and she wondered greatly at the dropping of his customary cool self-assurance which made her think that he might be piqued at her indifference to him, for even though she disliked him so excessively she was

22

honest enough to admit that his good looks and perfection of physique were such that his appeal would be
irresistible to ninety-nine women out of a hundred.

'Surely you're not dishonest enough to be telling me
it's the wrong conclusion?' he said tautly at last.

She swallowed, took a drink of her coffee and swallowed again. She was flustered and – much as she hated
having to confess it – rather overwhelmed by his
company in this lonely intimate place. It was the first
time they had met without there being others present; it
was also the first time he had troubled to open up a
conversation with her – if this near-slanging match
could be termed a conversation. Hitherto he had practically ignored her, the result of course of her own deliberate coldness towards him.

He was slanting her an interrogating glance, but she
failed to discover any tactful way of replying to his question and instead she bypassed it and said,

'Are you working, Mr. Lester?' Why didn't he clear
off and leave her to the peace she had been enjoying?

'No, I'm sitting here,' with heavy sarcasm that
brought a glint of fire to her eyes.

'I mean, were you working – before you came across
here?' Politeness demanded that she offer him some of
her coffee, but she hadn't another cup.

'I was surveying, yes. I'm clearing that scrub over
there to plant citrus trees.' Jill looked and frowned, but
bit back the protest that had risen swiftly to her lips.
The man had every right to do what he liked with his
own land, even if it did mean tearing up the natural
vegetation and spoiling the pretty vista which gave her
such pleasure when she looked from her bedroom

window. 'I asked you a question, Miss Sharman. Your evasion was starkly noticeable.'

'I—' She stopped, avoiding his gaze. 'What was the question?'

'I'll repeat it slowly.' And this he did, crushing her hopes of the subject's being dropped.

'What is it I don't like about you?' she repeated, forced, by some strange power he exerted, to meet his piercing gaze. 'Er – have I given that impression?' Her thoughts were on her brother and his wife, and the upset that would be caused to them if she and Dean were to reach the stage where their animosity became apparent.

Dean Lester made an exasperated click of his tongue.

'You disliked me intensely from the moment we met, so if you're honest you'll admit it instead of now making some endeavour to deny it.' She said nothing and he added, 'Are you too cowardly to answer me?'

'You're embarrassing me, Mr. Lester,' she flashed, more angry with herself than him, because of her inability to find some firm and pointed remark that would put an end to this persistence of his.

'I'm glad of it. Open dislike such as you've shown is an entirely new experience for me, and it's natural I should demand an explanation as to its cause.'

Demand . . . How like the man to use a word like that! However, unwilling as she was to bring about a further deterioration in her relationship with Dean, she said the only thing she could say.

'I'm sorry if I gave that impression, Mr. Lester. Please forget it.'

'So we're being tactful, eh? – and letting honesty go hang.' The mocking amusement returned to his voice and eyes; it grated, as did the idea of the apology she'd been forced to make just now. 'Were it not for your brother and his wife you'd open up and tell me exactly what you think about me.'

Jill's hackles rose; she put her empty cup on the grass beside her and stared straight at him.

'If we're to be so outspoken, Mr. Lester, then might I also inquire why you took an instant dislike to me?' Even before she uttered the final word he was shaking his head, faint contempt in his expression.

'No use,' he told her derisively, 'you can't switch the blame. The unfriendliness came entirely from you in the first place.' He seemed to inject a hint of boredom into his tones and she surmised he would very soon tire of the conversation and take himself off.

The conversation had surprised her, naturally, since Dean Lester had always seemed far too stiff and aloof to unbend in this way. Yet here he was, sitting comfortably against a tree, demanding to know the reason for her dislike of him. Dislike was a new experience, he had said, so it would appear that she was correct in her suspicion that he was piqued.

'I suppose,' she murmured, speaking her thoughts aloud, 'that you're so used to women falling all over you that you can't accept—' Horrified, she broke off, desiring nothing so much as to avoid those arrogant eyes and yet compelled by some force to meet their gaze. 'I – I . . .' What was there to say? She remained silent, unhappily aware that this time she must surely have damaged their relationship quite beyond repair.

She saw his brows come together, his mouth compress.

'No, Miss Sharman,' he returned acidly, 'as a matter of fact I'm not used to women falling all over me. However, I am used to being treated to civility—'

'I have never been uncivil, Mr. Lester,' she interrupted hastily. 'And as for that slip of the tongue—'

'Which was most illuminating,' he broke in before she could voice the intended apology. 'It reveals more than you think.'

'It does?' She stared blankly at him.

'Think about it,' he recommended. 'You'll then know what I mean.' He now appeared more than a little amused by his thoughts, for a smile of faint humour touched the fine outline of his mouth.

Jill did as he advised, but the light failed to dawn.

'Won't you explain what you meant?' she asked, her curiosity getting the better of her.

He hesitated a moment, a frown taking the place of his humour.

'No,' he decided at last, shaking his head. 'I won't explain. Forget it.'

She had no intention of forgetting it. Being all woman she possessed her share of curiosity and in spite of the firmness of his reply she was about to pursue the matter when suddenly a flash of comprehension made sense of his cryptic remark.

She had, by her mention of women falling all over him, admitted that he was an attractive man. And as she had shown an instant dislike of him he had concluded that it had been her intention right from the start not to be included in the type of woman she had mentioned.

Hence his statement that her slip of the tongue had been most illuminating. Her thoughts bringing colour even yet again to her cheeks, she tried to avoid those disconcerting eyes, but they held her gaze. Were his deductions correct? Had her instant dislike of him really been a defensive cloak? – donned in order that she would not fall victim to his undeniable charms? If so, it had not been a conscious act; as far as she knew the man had immediately struck her as one of those whose self-esteem and arrogance were to be deplored. She was a free-and-easy person herself and in consequence she had always been drawn to those of a similar nature. Dean Lester was the opposite in every way, there being no spontaneity about him, no swift manifestations of friendliness. Of course, she had to admit, on the occasion of their first meeting she herself had evinced no friendliness – quite the reverse, in fact, so perhaps there had been some excuse for his own cool impersonal manner.

'Would you like some coffee?' she asked in an endeavour to cover the embarrassment caused by her own deductions. 'I can wash my cup in the stream.'

'I have a flask with me, thank you,' he returned, still holding her gaze. She realized that in refusing to explain his enigmatic comments he had at least shown modesty; this much she had to grant him. 'How far are you riding?' he inquired at last, and she gave a small shrug.

'I don't know. I'm just exploring, and taking my time over it.' Both her attention and that of Dean were caught by a small flock of wild ducks that had flown over and settled on the small stony island formed by the braiding of the river just a short distance from the loop. The wet plumage on their breasts gleamed in the sunshine and their beaks flashed as they busily preened themselves.

'Exploring, eh?' Faintly he smiled, but the mockery had returned to his eyes. 'What do you expect to find?'

'Treasures in plenty – they're round every bend in the river.' Eagerness brought an enchanting smile to her lips; she forgot her animosity and added, 'You of course are used to it all, but to me there is still a great deal that is new. I want to discover it slowly, so that my pleasure is prolonged—' She stopped then, aware that she was running enthusiastically on and fearing that her companion might not be in the least interested.

His eyes flickered with a strange expression; she felt that everything about her was being examined and awkwardly she fluttered a hand to push back the bleached tendrils of hair from her face. It was a little nervous gesture, unconsciously made but one which seemed to give him cause to smile to himself.

'What are these treasures you are so fortunate to come across round every bend of the river?' he wanted to know at length, and in answer she made a spreading, comprehensive gesture with her hands.

'This, for example. Paradise in miniature – an island where nature lies undisturbed. Look at those orchids. Aren't they just too lovely? It's hard to believe they come under the order of parasites.'

Dean Lester's brows lifted a fraction. He appeared to be sending her a glance of censure.

'They don't; they're epiphytes. They derive their

food from the air.'

'They do? I always thought of them as taking their food from their hosts.'

'You should read up your botany,' he recommended. 'You'd be surprised how much more enjoyment you'd get from your explorations.' The carcase of a tree which had probably been struck by lightning lay rotting half in and half out of the river; small flowering plants grew healthily on it. 'Those are not parasites either. They also take their nourishment from the air.'

'Nature is marvellous,' breathed Jill, staring at the plants he indicated. 'Its wonders are everywhere!'

'Round every bend in the river,' he responded, and he laughed then and Jill looked fascinatedly into his face, intrigued by the transformation brought about by the laughter lines at the corners of his eyes.

Attractive . . .? Undoubtedly. He was watching her and she brought down her lashes to hide her expression. She had given enough away for one day. There was no sense in adding more air to his already inflated ego, she decided, and began packing her flask into the hessian bag she had brought with her, and which contained her sandwiches and the huge wedge of coconut cake which Lucie had insisted on including.

'I think I'll be on my way.' She felt unsure of herself, and angry because of it. 'I believe we're coming over to Nyala Mount tomorrow evening?'

He nodded.

'For dinner,' he told her briefly, and rose to his feet. She watched him take the leap across the stream, and this time there was no spiteful desire for him to miss the bank. Unloosing his horse, he sprang on to its back and, with a lift of the hand, he was gone. For a long while she listened, until the hoofbeats had died away in the silent distance. Pity he was so arrogant and sure of himself, seeming to accept as his right that he should be so wealthy and live in the most beautiful and imposing house in the district. Yes, it was a pity ... because otherwise he could be a rather pleasant neighbour to have.

CHAPTER TWO

At a quarter to eight the following evening Jill and her brother and his wife were entering the familiar drive of Nyala Mount. So many times they had travelled along it when the Fenwicks lived in the attractive white homestead now occupied by Dean Lester. Jill had always experienced pleasure on entering the drive where lovely dome palms swayed against the night sky and where heady perfumes were carried through the open windows of the station wagon. The palms were there, and the heady perfumes, but the pleasurable anticipation was absent. Jill had no enthusiasm for the evening in front of her.

Their host was waiting on the front stoep, impressive in white dinner jacket, one hand lightly resting half in and half out of his pocket, the other flat against one of the pillars of the stoep. The lights were all on, above and behind him. Jill knew she was being ungenerous and yet she said contemptuously to herself,

'He's like a priceless statue, on show and illuminated from all angles. He's only standing in that position for effect. Conceited creature!'

He came forward, suave, polite, and just a trifle cool. But the smile spelled welcome in just the correct amount; the expression in the grey eyes was one of pleasure at the arrival of his guests.

'Good evening, Lucie, and Bob. Miss Sharman . . .'

'Good evening, Mr. Lester,' came her automatic response, and she managed a thin smile as she looked up into that far too handsome face.

He was taking her wrap, and that of Lucie. A house-boy was standing by waiting to accept them from him.

Aperitifs were served on the stoep. Dean leant back in his chair and allowed his gaze to settle on Jill's face. Uncomfortable under the prolonged unsmiling stare, she adroitly managed to fit a word or two to the conversation taking place between Bob and Lucie, but she was acutely conscious of a half-smile appearing on Dean's lips and knew he was aware of her deliberate avoidance of his eyes. He was piqued and puzzled by her attitude; it was a pity, she thought, that he didn't begin to accept the fact that he was the kind of man she didn't happen to like. It was a pity he couldn't take a good look at himself through another person's eyes; he would then see that his type, while admittedly attractive to some people, could be most unattractive to others. The cool assured type, with superiority written all over them, and the condescending air that went with the superiority, had never appealed to Jill. She favoured the type matching her own nature and right from the start she had known that she and Dean Lester would never have anything in common, simply because she hated the discomfiture of feeling inadequate. It was a strain to try to keep level with him, as it were, and she failed to see any reason why she should be forced to endure that strain. It were far simpler to retire from this mental combat – or, better still, to avoid it altogether. At this stage she would never have admitted that her attitude might savour of the defensive – that, subconsciously, she had something to fear from allowing herself to become friendly with their magnificent neighbour. She was not ready to accept that the distance she kept was a safety measure against his attractiveness.

As for Dean himself, he appeared to adopt a similar attitude with her, but quite often she would suspect a hidden meaning beneath words that on the surface were dispassionate and spoken merely for the making of necessary conversation when the particular occasion in which they found themselves demanded it. He was experiencing something new, this he had admitted. And it was clear that he disliked intensely the new experience, and that he would change the relationship existing between him and Jill if he could.

At the dinner table he was the perfect host; the food put before his guests surpassed even that served up by Mrs. Fenwick, who excelled at cooking. To Jill it was just another black mark against him. Why, she thought disparagingly, did he have to outshine others in every single way?

Conversation was light, but when it flagged for a moment Jill looked up and Dean's eyes were fixed upon her. Silently she gritted her teeth. The man's interest constituted an annoyance and she heartily wished she had no other person to consider and that she could in consequence flash him the sort of glance that would have left him in no doubts about her opinion of him. But she was forced to respond when a smile touched his lips, and reply when he politely asked if he could refill her wineglass.

'Yes, please.'

Lucie also had a refill; she was a great favourite with

Dean, speaking the same language, since of course, she too was a South African. They had both lived at one time in Pretoria, and, therefore, would at times go off for a while on a subject in which Bob and his sister were unable to join. But this was seldom, and Dean would with his innate good manners very soon veer the conversation so as to include his other two guests.

On those numerous occasions when they had dined with the Fenwicks there had come the inevitable suggestion of a stroll in the grounds after dinner, for the Fenwicks were great walkers. To Jill's surprise Dean made a similar suggestion. She had no wish to walk because she was sure she would find herself beside him and she so disliked having to tilt her head to look up at him – which she surmised she would be forced to do as they conversed. She always felt insignificant when having to do this, and she also sensed that Dean rather liked being looked up to!

'Do you mind if I just sit on the stoep?' she asked. 'I feel rather tired this evening.'

Bob and Lucie looked a trifle concerned.

'You work too hard,' Bob admonished. 'Why didn't you follow my advice and have one of the boys help you with that herbaceous border? You can't bend your back all day and not suffer for it.'

'I haven't got the backache,' she instantly protested. 'It's just that I shall enjoy myself better sitting on the stoep than walking.'

'All right,' shrugged Bob. 'We'll not stay away long.'

Dean hesitated, but decided to remain silent, and Jill watched the three go off along the path which led to a lovely area of wild garden. At their disappearance she relaxed, but there was something not quite right about Nyala Mount now that the Fenwicks had been replaced as owners by the cold and arrogant Dean Lester.

Suddenly she heard footsteps drawing nearer and was filled with the uneasy expectation of something unpleasant. Nyala Mount's owner returning . . .

'Where are Bob and Lucie?' she asked the moment she saw him coming up the steps.

'They've carried on for a while.' He got so far and then swung lightly over the rail, landing a few feet away from where she sat. 'I decided my manners were lacking in leaving one of my guests to entertain herself, so I returned.' Dean actually laughed with his eyes. 'You might at least register gratitude for my return even if you can't show any sign of pleasure.'

She cast him a swift glance. This mood was decidedly new.

'You place me in an awkward position,' she responded, deciding that as he had dropped diplomacy there was no reason why she should not do the same.

'Do I?' Dean looked down at her and his firm mouth twitched. 'Jill Sharman, you're a strange girl. But don't let me divert you. Carry on with what's in your mind. I'm more than eager to hear it.'

She coloured slightly and his eyes flickered as they noted the delightful contrast now between rosy cheeks and the pale ivory of her wide unlined forehead.

'Very well, Mr. Lester, I'll be quite honest and tell you that I'm not in the least grateful for your return. I was content to be alone for a short while.'

The humour faded from his face. Bringing up a chair

by flicking the cane under-support with the toe of his shoe, he sat down.

'That remark,' he told her with cold severity, 'went some considerable way beyond the border of tact; it was downright rude.'

The rosy colour deepened and spread. Jill lowered her eyelashes.

'I'm sorry, Mr. Lester—'

'Dean's the name. Sorry if it hasn't the strong masculine sound of Robert and Richard and James, but my mother's favourite grandpa was an American.'

She rather liked the name of Dean, but not for anything would she make the admission.

'It sounds American,' was all she said, glad that her apology had passed practically unnoticed. She would have hated him to comment on it, causing her embarrassment because the comment was sure to have been edged with mockery.

'It's old English, actually; means a valley-dweller, so you see it fits me well enough.' He leant back in his chair and regarded her critically. 'You're not in the least tired,' he pronounced chidingly. 'What made you tell the fib?'

She said abruptly,

'Tell me, Mr. Lester—'

'Dean,' he softly interrupted.

Jill gave an audible sigh.

'What does it profit you to try and disconcert me all the time?'

'Shouldn't you have used the word "satisfaction"?'

'Very well. What satisfaction does it afford you?'

'None as yet, because I haven't succeeded in disconcerting you, but I will,' he added with a sort of amused warning. 'By the way, I never discovered what it is you don't like about me?'

'I said I was sorry if I gave that impression,' she reminded him.

'One day I expect you'll open up and tell me,' he said musingly.

So he had no intention of acknowledging her efforts at evasion.

'You're an unusual man, Mr. Lester.' Jill sent him a challenging look, saw the satirical expression appear as he teetered back in his chair.

'I asked why you'd told that fib,' he said, ignoring her statement. 'Was it in order to be relieved of my company for a space?'

'You're my host, Mr. Lester. Please don't expect me to say things I'll regret.'

To her surprise he laughed.

'This time at least you're honest. So you admit you made the excuse of being tired, merely in order to be spared the ordeal of walking with me? There were the others, you know. It wouldn't have been the ordeal you imagined.'

Naturally this sent her into confusion, but she managed to retain a veneer of composure, and even to inject a tone of lightness into her voice.

'You've become inordinately interested in me all at once, Mr. Lester. I'm extremely puzzled by this interest.'

'Not interested, Jill,' he corrected, 'but intrigued. 'I'm sure you're a nice girl basically—' He stopped and smiled in some amusement because she was blushing and at the same time shaking her head in protest. 'Yes, a nice girl basically, but with me you're – well—' He stopped again and directed his gaze at her. 'Shall I be blunt?'

'By all means,' she readily encouraged, a sudden curiosity gripping her.

'With me you're just about as bitchy as you dare be.'

Her chin lifted; she gave him a kindling look.

'Now *you* have disregarded the borderline of tact! That was the rudest thing that has ever been said to me!'

'I'm glad I said it,' was his unexpected response. 'It produced some emotion in you. You're rather pretty when you're angry, Jill; your eyes sparkle and your lips quiver. I'm glad they don't go tight, for there's nothing more ugly than a tight-lipped woman.'

What was all this about? Jill's anger subsided on the instant; she was aware of a strange tingling of her pulse. She felt she must watch her step or otherwise she would be simpering under the man's flattery as, she surmised, many other women had simpered under it, for there was no denying that flattery coming from a man like Dean Lester was more than a little gratifying.

'I think,' she said springing up, 'that I'll go for a stroll after all.'

Sardonic humour brought a swift curve to his mouth.

'Coward . . .' he murmured in his deep and attractive tones. 'Sit down and persevere. You could contribute to a friendly conversation were you to put a little effort into it.'

Jill frowned at him suspiciously.

'What exactly are you trying to do, Mr. Lester?' she inquired coolly after a pause.

'Establish a neighbourly relationship between us. Has it not struck you that your brother and his wife must inevitably realize, before very long, that you and I are near enemies?' Despite the content of his words his voice was pleasantly conversational and he had her mystified.

'Are we unneighbourly?' was all she could find to say, and was not in the least surprised on seeing his brows lift with impatience.

'I said near enemies, Jill,' he reminded her, the steely intentness of his eyes matching the impatience evident in his tones, and that lift of his brows. 'Are we to continue like this indefinitely?'

She was at a loss and it annoyed her to know that Dean was well aware of this.

'I suppose,' she conceded at length, 'that we could adopt a more amicable manner with one another.'

His lips twitched.

'What you need,' he declared softly, 'is chastening. You're far too perverse for a woman.'

Jill's brown eyes sparkled; the 'trusting, faithful dog' expression of which her father had so often spoken was totally lacking at this moment.

'What you need, Mr. Lester,' she said quiveringly, 'is to receive a set-down! You're far too conceited and filled with a sense of your own superiority!'

'So that's how you think of me?'

'Surely you know your own character?'

'Know thyself,' he quoted in reflective tones. 'I

wonder how many of us do know ourselves?' He was still sitting down, while Jill stood by the rail of the patio. Dean pressed a toe to the floor and thrust back his chair, an action that brought the hint of a smile to her face, as it was abundantly plain that he disliked the necessity of looking up at her. 'I'm conceited,' he mused, frowning slightly, 'and I'm filled with a sense of my own superiority.'

Jill coloured at the idea of her downright rudeness. It was unlike her, and she felt angry that he had the ability of bringing out the worst in her the way he had on more than one occasion.

'Perhaps we should put an end to this conversation,' she suggested. 'I'll go and see where Bob and Lucie have got to.' She hoped he would not offer to accompany her and was presently relieved to note the unresponsive mask of his face.

'Did it not occur to you, Jill, to ask yourself the reason for my statement that you needed chastening?' Automatically she shook her head and he continued, 'I said it to bring home to you the fact that you alone are responsible for the very unfriendly relationship which has developed between us.' His tones had an edge to them; his mouth was set, matching the sudden tautness of his jaw.

Jill averted her head; she had received a rebuke and it went right home, since she was honest enough to admit that she alone had begun all this, because of the instant dislike she had taken to the man.

'I suppose I should apologize,' she began when almost roughly he interrupted her.

'Don't trouble, not if it's so grudgingly made.' He

gave an imperious gesture with his hand. 'Go and find your brother and Lucie. My presence is obviously annoying you.'

For a moment she hesitated, aware all at once that she now had no inclination to do as she was told. On the contrary, she would have liked to remain, and to find some way of repairing this added damage to their relationship. But the dark lean face, inscrutable and tight, was so forbidding that she turned from it, and took the patio steps rather quickly, so as to remove even her back from the anger in those steely grey eyes.

It was an hour later that she began to panic, marvelling that she could have got lost.

'This is ridiculous,' she repeatedly murmured as she went in one direction and then, turning, took another. 'I can't be far away. It's just that I can't get my bearings because the trees are so scattered, and they're masking the lights of Dean's homestead.'

Her heart was slowly coming up into her throat; her breath was uneven, her legs were becoming weak as panic increased. Supposing she were out here on the veld all night! It didn't bear thinking about, and yet she found she could think of nothing else. All was so very dark, with not the merest hint of the purple glow so often seen long after the sun had gone down. It seemed to linger for a long while, disappearing only on those nights when the moon was full. The trees were dark nebulous masses, the kopjes inky mounds barely discernible against the background of an unlit sky.

She had called out many times, but realized she had not done this soon enough. And the reason for this was her reluctance to allow Dean Lester to know she was lost. He would gloat, she knew, and would subject her to some more of his sarcasm and mocking amusement. No, she had decided, she would find her way back, and pretend she had so enjoyed the solitude that she had continued to walk on and on. Now, however, she bitterly regretted her obstinacy, for she was in a much worse position than she would have been then. She was lost, and she felt instinctively that she was a long way from Nyala Mount. If only she had not been so averse to calling out, much sooner, then undoubtedly she would have been heard.

'It would have been so humiliating,' she said. 'He'd have gloated—' Her thoughts were sharply cut off as she thought she heard a call, and she stood still, every nerve in her body alert. No . . . she had been mistaken. Her spirits sank again and her heart throbbed against her ribs. How long had she been out here? she wondered. She had been trying to keep up a calculation as she went along, and now she estimated she had been out here for about an hour and a half. How could she have got out of calling range? It had been her stupidity and pride that had prevented an earlier call and she must have been going farther and farther away from Nyala Mount all the time.

She dwelt on the anxiety she must be causing the three people at the house. Bob and Lucie would certainly be troubled, but she revised her idea that Dean also would be anxious. He would more likely be furious at having to go out and search for her, regarding her as a nuisance more than anything else. She wandered on, calling and calling, and hoping that by some miracle she was travelling in the right direction. She was beginning to feel the effect of her own anxiety and she began to be a little sick inside. She was thirsty too, and felt clammy and cold. Shivers ran through her after a while and there was a faint rushing noise in her head.

'A rest wouldn't do me any harm,' she said, and sat down with her back against a tree. Everything was so silent and still; it was an oppressive deathlike hush which seemed to overwhelm the entire land all around her. An indefinable scent pervaded the air, heady and overpowering like an anaesthetic . . .

For a long time she managed to shake off her drowsiness, realizing how important it was to keep her ears alert, and also to call out at fairly regular intervals. But the silence and the persistent aroma proved too strong for her and her eyelids began to droop. Her voice when she called became weaker and weaker; her legs protested when in a final endeavour she rose from her sitting position with the intention of keeping on walking and in this way preventing herself from falling asleep. How long she managed to continue in this half-asleep condition she never knew; she eventually estimated she had been out in the bushveld for more than three hours.

Once again she thought she heard a call and actually managed to shout, her strength supported by fear. No answering call was heard and with black dismay she knew she was again imagining things. If only she knew which way to go! But with not a landmark visible she could be putting more and more distance between her and the homestead and at last she owned that the most sensible course was to stay where she was. And so she sat down again, after picking her way through some spiny undergrowth towards a huge mahogany tree where, as before, she sought the support of the trunk for her back.

The silence was no more; the nocturnal life of the bushveld was all around her and sounds mingled with one another so that it seemed a thousand voices were blending as one. Leaves rustled on the ground, causing her heart to stop beating for a terrified second as she thought of snakes. This realization of the life existing in the darkness prevented her calling out any more. She had no wish to attract attention to herself.

Her head drooped to one side; she felt strangely calm all at once, and pleasantly restful. The shivers had ceased and so had the rushing noise in her head. Her eyes closed and opened several times, but the pressure of sleep was on her, defeating her already weakened senses, and soon all consciousness was blotted out.

CHAPTER THREE

THE murmur of a breeze awoke her and she sat up, shivering in the misty chill of dawn. A drab grey light came from over the kopje, breaking the dark mass of trees into individual shapes as it filtered through the boughs. A bird twittered, then another and another, the chorus rising to a crescendo as the grey of dawn gave way to fawn and yellow, heralds of the glory to come. Jill stood up, stiff and icy cold, her clothes damp and clinging. They would soon dry, once the sun was up, but she was thirsty, and still tired, despite her sleep.

Which way to go? If only she could find the river she would then be able to discover some landmarks, whether these be upstream or down. She had a full day in which to get home and she felt this would be comparatively easy if only the river would come into view. She would travel downstream for a few miles and then, if she did not find her bearings, she would retrace her steps and travel upstream, when she must eventually find herself on familiar ground.

The only trouble was that she felt weak already, and the thought of the search seemed too much for her and it took all her determination not to sink down again and have another sleep.

The world around her was alive, vibrating, the air filled with the delicious scent of growing things. Slopes became vivid patches of colour as the sun's crimson rays intruded into the fawns and yellows and opals, soon dispersing them altogether until the whole exotic scene was a dazzling blaze of light which gave an almost unearthly enchantment to the distant line of tree-clothed hills. On another high bluff every shade of green was picked out by the play of light and shade as a film of cloud, fine as lace, drifted across the sun. Jill stood gazing around, appreciative, even in these circumstances, of the sheer perfection spread all about her. But the harmony and peace of the bushveld did not remain with her for long; she soon found herself anxiously wondering if she would discover her way home or, alternatively, whether someone would come upon her in their search. For obviously a search party would be out, and she dared not think of all the trouble she was causing.

By noon she was so greatly alarmed that she could scarcely think clearly. There was no sign of the river, and she despaired of finding it in time to get home before darkness fell. But, tired though she was, with hunger added to her thirst, she kept trudging on and on, hoping that by some stroke of luck she would come upon the river. And it was while she was hesitating, wondering whether or not to carry straight on, that she noticed what was unmistakably the remnants of an abandoned meander core. Her heart leapt as she realized that at least here was a relic which proved that the river was somewhere about. And as she stood and stared she realized also that she was standing on a river terrace and, looking down below, she saw the eroded remains of another, abandoned a long time ago when, having undergone the process of rejuvenation, the river had cut itself a deeper channel, leaving behind the original bank, above the present one. The two terraces gave evidence of two such rejuvenations and it was easy to see in which direction she must travel. With hope and optimism giving her renewed strength, she set off, not too quickly, for she was well aware that she would tire more readily if she proceeded at a brisk pace. But her thirst was beginning to cause her extreme discomfort and she did wonder if she would in the end succumb to the sweltering heat which was already causing the entire landscape to shimmer under its haze.

The afternoon wore on and it was not until four o'clock that she found the river and even then it was still some distance away. The sight of the water gleaming through the trees spurred her on and no sooner had she reached the bank than she was lying full length on her stomach, cupping the cool crystal water in her hands and thirstily drinking it. Ah, that was better! She felt she could do without food for a long time yet, so long as she had water. Which way must she go? She felt that whichever she chose it would be the wrong choice. Still, at least she had the river, and she knew that both Bob's farm and Dean Lester's home were not far from its banks.

Better continue calling out, she decided, as she had been calling out at intervals all the time. Not once had she even thought she heard a response, and this convinced her that she had been moving away from both homesteads all the while.

Her calls became weaker; she felt exhaustion creeping on and at last she was forced to rest. The shadows grew longer, transforming the hills into grotesque shapes; clouds laced the opal sky as daylight began to retreat before the swiftly-approaching twilight. The sun turned red, dropping with an arc of flame in its wake, and very soon the violet glow of dusk hung fleetingly over the silent bushland. Jill trembled from head to foot as hope fled. She made a desperate attempt to thrust out the thought that she might die here, alone by the river, but found it impossible to do so. For it now seemed that she was never to find her way home since she lacked the strength to retrace her steps and go up river. She had chosen to go down river and now felt convinced she had made the wrong choice, as she had at first felt sure she would.

Her lids drooped and she felt her senses drifting away. Was she to go into a coma? Vaguely the idea emerged from the condition of dull obscurity that was fast drawing her into its net. A coma . . .

The shout, a long way off, galvanized her into action and she sprang to her feet with a spurt of strength which she would never have believed possible, not the way she felt. But hope was the source of her energy and she began running in the direction from which the shout had come, calling as she went.

'I'm here! – *here*!'

No response, and she realized her voice was no louder than a small child's. Her throat was aching, the after-math of its parched condition before she at last located the river, and she found it impossible to shout. If she should lose whoever it was she would surely die, for they might not come this way again. She called repeatedly and her heart missed a beat when at length she heard Dean Lester's voice, still a long way off, but close enough now for her to recognize it.

'Jill – Jill! Where are you? Keep on calling!'

She did as she was told, but her strength was failing and she sank down in the long grasses. She heard the voice again, but was unable to respond as her senses were leaving her. The grass hurt her arms and legs, scratching them as she fell on her side. She heard the night sounds, saw the hills and the trees merge into an unrecognizable mass . . . and then she heard and saw no more until, an hour later, she opened her eyes and a swift glance round the room told her where she was, as she had been in the room before, several times when Mrs. Fenwick was down with a fever. Lucie's anxious face was above her, but she said nothing, merely giving Jill some sort of milk food which she put to her lips with a spoon.

It was considerably later still when, on opening her eyes again, she saw Dean standing above her. He looked so grim and cold and forbidding that she turned her head away, conscious of the fact that she wanted to cry, although for what reason she was unable to say since she was no longer suffering any discomfort.

'How are you feeling?' The tones were rough and stern. She suspected she would later receive a scold.

'My head aches dreadfully.' She stared up at him, apology in her eyes. 'I'm so sorry . . .'

'I'll get you something for your head,' he said, and left the room. On his return he held a glass in his hand. 'Sit up.' She did as she was told and he gave her two tablets and the water.

'Thank you.' A pause. 'What happened?'

He raised his brows.

'We were out looking for you, naturally.'

Jill bit her lip guiltily.

'I'm so sorry,' she repeated, convinced she would never live down the disgrace.

Dean said tautly,

'You were in a temper when you went off—'

'No! Why should you say that?'

A click of asperity with his tongue was her only answer for a space and then Dean went on,

'Obviously you can't abide the sight of me. And if your dislike is so strong that it induces you to escape from my company at any cost, then the wise course is for us not to see each other unless it's absolutely necessary.' He paused, looking down at her, his stern angular features a mask of inscrutability. 'I shall naturally have to include you in any future invitations to Bob and Lucie, but I suggest you find some excuse for declining. I in my turn will make every endeavour to avoid annoying you with my presence.'

If anything could have made Jill feel more blameworthy than she felt already it was this statement by the man who had organized her rescue. She would have died had he not found her, as she had no doubts whatsoever about her failing strength. Looking up into his set face, its arrogant lines very much in evidence as he in turn stared down at her, she endeavoured vainly to find words that would aptly convey her deep gratitude. For no matter what her opinion of Dean – her dislike of his arrogance and superior air – she was most naturally fully conscious of what she owed him. But try as she would she found difficulty in articulating words, especially when Dean was so stern and accusing in his manner towards her.

After a long uncomfortable silence she was able to

say,

'How long must I stay here—?' And then she broke off, aware of the sheer ingratitude which must seem to be outstandingly apparent in her question.

'You should be able to leave later today,' he snapped and, taking the glass in which he had brought her the water, he turned abruptly away and strode from the room.

Abject misery engulfed her – misery which on examination appeared to be quite out of proportion. Why should Dean's manner *hurt*? That it should give her cause for dejection was natural, simply because she herself was responsible for it in that she had appeared to be quite lacking in gratitude for what he had done. But that his manner should hurt was a circumstance she failed to understand.

It certainly did hurt, though. Also, the idea of his avoiding her, deliberately, and of her having to refuse his invitations, actually added to her hurt. This, after she had previously wanted nothing so much as to be able to find an excuse for keeping away from Nyala Mount.

With these puzzling thoughts flitting about in her mind she gradually dozed, and was awakened more than five hours later by the entry into her room of Olive, the only female among Dean's servants. Being a legacy from the Fenwicks she was known to Jill, who sat up and smiled at her as she came towards the bed.

'You have slept a long time.' The impassive dusky face was above her as Jill looked up. 'The baas would not have me disturb you for your lunch. You are hungry now?'

'I could eat something, yes.'

'I came because you have a visitor.'

'A visitor?' Lucie and Bob would walk right in. 'Who is it?'

'Mr. Mason, he says his name is. Baas Lester is out in the fields and does not know of this visitor. Shall I let him come to you?'

'Yes, of course.'

'Very good, Miss Sharman.'

A couple of minutes later Patrick walked in. He looked anxious, but not excessively so. And his ready smile appeared just as soon as he saw that Jill had suffered very little from her ordeal.

'I heard about it through one of our boys who is brother of one of Dean Lester's,' he explained when Jill had inquired how he had come to know that she had been lost. 'How are you feeling?'

'I'm all right, thank you, Patrick.'

'You don't look at all bad.' He shook his head. 'How the dickens did you manage to get lost?'

'Don't ask me,' she pleaded. 'I was deep in thought and just wandered. It's more easy to get lost than I realized, and it won't ever happen again, I can assure you. I feel dreadful about the trouble I've caused.'

Patrick merely shrugged. Like everything else, he took the matter lightly, saying that as long as she had been found there was no sense in wasting time on regrets and self-recrimination.

'This is a real plush establishment,' he observed, glancing round. 'Dean Lester must have paid the earth for the place.'

'He's a very wealthy planter,' she returned. 'He owns several other forests, so I've heard.'

'Lucky man.' Patrick took another look around. 'It's a wonder he's not married,' he commented at length. 'Must be over thirty, I should think.'

'He doesn't appear to be interested in women. I expect his trees give him everything he wants,' she added unthinkingly, and Patrick suddenly roared with laughter. Jill herself had to join in, for as always Patrick's particular brand of laughter was infectious. And it was just at this moment that Dean chose to enter the room, having been informed by Olive that Jill had a visitor.

For a long moment he stood just inside the door, his angular face set, his grey eyes like points of cold steel. Jill's laugh died on her lips. Patrick on the other hand merely paused before breaking into renewed laughter. Jill became angry; she spoke hastily, beginning to introduce the two men, but was interrupted by Dean, who said, his voice cold as the expression in his eyes,

'We've met.' From Patrick he transferred his gaze to Jill, sitting up in bed, attired in the bright cotton nightdress which she had previously surmised had been borrowed from Olive. 'I believe you'd like some lunch?'

'If – it won't be—'

'—any trouble?' with a slant of an eyebrow and a crisp inflection in his voice. 'I'll tell Olive to come and see what you want.' As yet he hadn't spoken a word to Patrick, who – it suddenly occurred to Jill – should have sought out Dean and asked his permission before entering one of his bedrooms. The sudden realization of this breach of etiquette, for which she herself was equally responsible, caused the colour to fluctuate in Jill's cheeks. Dean saw it, and watched it impassively for a

53

space before turning his attention to her visitor. 'Perhaps you will leave when Miss Sharman's lunch is brought in? I've just received a message from her sister-in-law that she and her husband will be over in about an hour's time – to take Miss Sharman home.' Without waiting for an answer he left the room; Patrick's half-humorous eyes followed him and he had scarcely closed the door behind him before the young man said, in quite a loud voice which, thought Jill, must surely carry to the man who had just left,

'What's soured him, suddenly? Or is he always like this? I've never had much to do with him – merely seeing him at the club and at one or two meetings we've had at various times.'

'I expect he was not too pleased at my having a visitor,' was all Jill could think of saying in reply. 'After all, this is his house, and my presence here must be causing him inconvenience. The least I could have done was to send Olive to find him before inviting you in here.' Her voice was deeply troubled, but Patrick remained unconcerned. There was no harm in her having a visitor, he maintained, and added, bringing a sudden frown to Jill's flushed face,

'Or a dozen visitors for that matter. It isn't doing him any harm.'

To Jill's relief her lunch arrived and Patrick said good-bye and left. An hour later Lucie and Bob arrived with the station wagon and within fifteen minutes Jill was in it and being driven home. It was most significant that Dean had not offered to drive her home in his luxurious car; Jill knew for sure that this courtesy would have been extended to her – if only to save her brother the trouble of coming for her – if it hadn't been for that breach of etiquette over Patrick's visit.

Over a month had gone by since Jill had got lost. Dean, true to his word, had kept out of her way, while Jill herself had made excuses not to accompany her brother and Lucie when they went over to Nyala Mount. That they were beginning to display some puzzlement was only to be expected, and Jill did wonder just how long it would be before she and Dean could conceal from them the animosity existing between the timber man and herself.

As time went on Jill was forced to own that the animosity she had felt against Dean was swiftly fading; she was ever conscious of what he had done for her and that but for him she must surely have died out there in the lonely bushveld. She felt she had repaid him in the most shoddy fashion and whenever she brought to mind that visit of Patrick's, his laughter and the words he had uttered as Dean left the room, she went hot all over and futilely wished she could turn back the clock so that she could have acted differently, doing what Dean would have expected her to do and asking his permission before inviting a near stranger into the bedroom.

She and he were forced to meet one evening when the three from Bangali Farm attended a dance at the Springbok Club in Breysburg. Dean was there and he naturally joined his friends from Bangali when they were over at the bar.

His greeting was cordial; his nod for Jill swift and indifferent. He asked what they were all having and bought the drinks. He leant negligently against the bar, one arm resting along it. Immaculate in a white tropical suit, his bronzed skin shining and a lazy expression in his grey eyes, he was about as handsome a man as it was possible to find; Jill was forced to admit this. His air of distinction and faint hauteur set him above every other man in the room, including Bob, who himself was both good-looking and well above average height.

Jill felt awkward, for not once was she addressed by Dean. His attention was with Bob and Lucie and as they did not notice that Jill was being left out of the conversation she found herself wishing she had stayed at home. But the evening was only just beginning and immediately Patrick and his family arrived Jill excused herself and went over to join them at a table where the waiter brought them drinks. Others straggled in, and after a while the buffet tables were surrounded. Jill and Patrick went over together, choosing sandwiches and delicious pastries. They sat down on rattan chairs and chatted as they ate.

'Shall we dance?' Patrick asked when at last they had finished. 'I hope you'll not complain if I miss a step or two; I twisted my ankle this morning doing a silly thing. I took the verandah steps at one jump.'

Jill thought of Dean, making that tremendous leap across the river and landing with all the ease and grace of a practised athlete.

Patrick missed more than a step or two – and his mistakes were several times noticed by Dean, much to Jill's vexation. She had never enjoyed a dance less, nor felt so embarrassed. Dean's glance, half contemptuous, half amused, stung her beyond all reason. She blushed hotly and was inordinately relieved when the music stopped and she was able to sink into one of the sofas at one end of the big hall. Bob came for the next dance, and then one or two other neighbours came along. Unconsciously Jill was waiting for Dean. Why should she want to dance with him? It would be embarrassing; they would dance in total silence and she would be glad when the dance was over . . .

She gave a deep sigh, and her partner, Charles Goulding from a farm five miles to the west of Dean's plantation boundary, looked at her with an expression of inquiry.

But she remained quiet and Charles began talking of trivialities in the pleasantly conversational manner usual on such occasions as this buffet and informal dance, which was typical of many held at the club.

At last Dean approached her, suavely inviting her to dance. Once on the floor, away from anyone who might happen to overhear him, Dean made a terse apology for asking her to dance.

'For appearances' sake,' he explained, 'I had to come over to you. Bob and Lucie were becoming puzzled – and a trifle upset, I think. It looked as if I were being unneighbourly.' Leaning away from her slightly, he added, 'I hope you can bear it for a few minutes?' A short pause and then, when Jill found nothing to say, 'At least you won't have the annoyance of my treading on your toes, or tripping you up.'

Colour appeared in her cheeks.

'Patrick's hurt his ankle,' she submitted rather tersely.

'Then the sensible thing is to rest it,' with deep sarcasm which, strangely, failed to elicit any swift retort from Jill. She had done enough damage already; and she herself was the loser by it. For it was far from comfortable being left out of the conversation as she had been, and in addition she had recently wanted to accept Dean's invitations and yet she was forced to decline them, because he had told her to. In consequence she was left alone at the farm, having to amuse herself with a book – on which she would invariably be unable to concentrate because her thoughts would keep switching to Dean and what was going on at Nyala Mount. On two occasions he had given a rather large dinner party and Jill would thoroughly have enjoyed being one of the guests. But once again she was forced to make an excuse for not going. Bob had remarked on it this time, though guardedly, as neither he nor Lucie ever interfered in Jill's action – not any more now than they did at first, during those difficult months of readjustment when Jill had so often behaved in a rather unorthodox manner.

'You never accept Dean's invitations these days? I seem always to be making excuses for your non-appearance.'

'It so happens that I always have a headache, or feel off colour in some other way.'

Bob had shrugged and let it pass at that. But Jill knew that he and Lucie must very soon realize that she was deliberately avoiding Dean – if they hadn't already done so.

Suddenly aware that the music had stopped. Jill looked up at her partner. His face was taut, his eyes held an expression of indifference.

'Thank you,' he said crisply, and as they were already at the edge of the dance floor, he made a slight bow and left her. And at that moment four late arrivals appeared and as she watched, Dean strode over to them. She saw him shake hands with one of the men and with a tall girl, slender and elegant and beautifully groomed. Jill didn't know whether it was her imagination, but Dean and the girl seemed to keep their hands in one another's for rather longer than was necessary. The adept way the girl managed to flaunt her beauty before Dean's eyes was most certainly not imagination.

'Know who she is?' Patrick was at Jill's side, his eyes following the direction of her gaze.

'No; is she staying with the Drakes?'

'I expect so; she came with them.' Patrick turned to a young man standing close. 'Wally, do you know who the glamorous girl is?' With a flick of his finger he indicated the fascinating creature who was still looking up at Dean. 'She's certainly got what it takes!'

'I agree.' He spoke softly, with a ring of admiration in his tone. Glancing round, Jill noticed that almost every male in the room had his eyes on the newcomer.

'She and her uncle are guests of the Drakes. The girl's recently been jilted, and is heartbroken. She lives with her uncle, and as he's fairly well off he decided to bring her here to his friend's farm just to help her get over it.'

'She was jilted?' echoed Patrick unbelievingly. 'Who in his right mind would jilt a devastatingly beautiful girl like that? She's one in a million!'

'Undoubtedly. They don't come like that every day.' A small pause as, becoming aware of Jill's presence, the young man turned politely, so as to include her in the conversation. 'She appears to be getting on all right with

Dean Lester, though,' he added with a faint laugh. 'Perhaps he'll help mend her broken heart.'

'It's damned hard on a girl when she's thrown over.' Patrick seemed quite unable to take his eyes off the girl's lovely face. 'I must get an introduction.'

Meanwhile, having suddenly realized his omission, Patrick introduced Jill to the young man, Wally Maitland from a citrus farm some thirty miles distant.

'You'd like an introduction to Miss de Courcy?' Wally then asked Patrick, who instantly said yes, most certainly he would.

'I didn't realize you knew her personally,' he added.

'I happened to drop in at the Drakes' just after the arrival of Sylvia de Courcy and her uncle,' he explained. 'It was Mrs. Drake who told me of the girl's broken engagement. She seemed dreadfully upset – Sylvia, I mean.' He looked at Jill as he added, 'Come on, then, and I'll introduce you.'

Jill had no option than to accompany him and Patrick over to the bar, where the party now was. Dean's eyes met Jill's for an indifferent moment just as she and Sylvia were shaking hands, but then Dean's full attention became fixed on the girl who, appearing rather fragile and sad, produced a quivering smile which soon fluttered towards Dean. Something strange stirred within Jill; she knew she ought to be feeling compassion for the girl – but she was not. In fact, amazing as it was, she failed to summon up even the smallest degree of sympathy for her.

Dean bought a round of drinks, and the party, now consisting of eight people, occupied one of the larger tables over by the wall. The lights were soft and intimate; Dean and the beautiful Sylvia were seated side by side under one of them and in its flattering glow the girl's beauty took on an ethereal quality. Another glance around disclosed the fact that a good deal of male attention was still centred on Sylvia de Courcy. In fact, thought Jill, she was taking the place by storm.

'Shall we dance?' The suave polite voice of Dean caught Jill's ears from out of the general conversation going on at the table. Slanting the girl a glance, Jill saw the flutter of long dark lashes, the quiver of full red lips.

The two drifted away; Wally caught Patrick's eye and winked. Jill's own eyes were drawn to the couple, both so handsome and arresting that attention was inevitably centred on them as they danced. A strange dryness had settled in Jill's throat and she found herself unable to take any further part in the conversation going on around her.

CHAPTER FOUR

THE bushveld was silent, as if overawed by the brilliance of the moon, an enormous moon whose light outshone the stars so that the nearest to it could not be seen.

Jill and Patrick had come out into the wild gardens of the club, the air inside having become hot and overpowering. They strolled about, chatting pleasantly, but Jill's mind was all the time abstractedly occupied by the mental picture of Dean and Sylvia, dancing – for almost every dance they had got up together – with all eyes on them, eyes wide with admiration, for not only were they arresting in their appearance, but they danced superbly – like professionals who had practised together incessantly. Dean seemed fascinated by the girl, who would look up into his face and produce that melancholy smile which in itself was oddly alluring.

'There they go!' from Patrick with a distinct sigh edging his words. 'What chance does a fellow like me have beside a bloke like Dean Lester? Broken heart or no, she looked to me to be smitten with him at the first glance.'

Pulse tingling, Jill allowed her gaze to follow the indication of her companion's raised hand. Dean and Sylvia had taken another path through the gardens, a path which skirted the open veld and wound away into the wall of dark green trees marking the limit of the club grounds. Here vegetation was fairly dense, with giant cedars being almost suffocated by the ruthless tentacles of epiphytic fig trees winding around trunk and branches alike. The undergrowth was thick with forest growth, but a path had been cut through it and, so Jill had been told, the walk along this path was most pleasant.

And more pleasant in the moonlight, mused Jill, her gaze following until the couple were eventually lost to view.

Dean ... to be interested so quickly. She had told Patrick that he didn't bother very much with women – had intimated that his work fulfilled his needs. And now here he was, attracted to the lovely Sylvia on sight, so much so that he had monopolized her ever since.

'Do you mind if we go back?' Impulsively she turned to Patrick, stopping as she did so. 'I – I don't feel like walking.' What was the matter with her? she asked herself angrily. Why were strange tremors affecting her nerves? Why was it that she just hated the idea of being out here with Patrick, while Sylvia was over there, in the intimacy of the forest, with the man whom she, Jill, disliked intensely—? But no; she had been vaguely aware for some time that she no longer disliked him.

But it had taken the appearance on the scene of the beautiful and appealing Sylvia de Courcy for Jill fully to realize that her dislike of Dean had not only disappeared, but that it had left in its place something entirely different.

The admission robbed her temporarily of the ability to feel or think properly, so devastating was the mental shock she sustained on realizing the import of what she had accepted. Dean, of all men! Not only would he have been unattainable in the ordinary way, but his remoteness had been increased a thousandfold by her own creation of the yawning rift that now existed between them.

'You want to go back to that hot room – already?' Patrick looked at her in a puzzled way. 'Aren't you feeling well?'

'Not very,' she replied unthinkingly, and he immediately pointed out that the fresh air was, in that case, far preferably to the less healthy atmosphere of the crowded club room.

'There's a seat over there, under the tree.' As he was already moving towards it Jill allowed herself to follow, although for the first time she was irritated by her companion. He treated everything so lightly – even her statement that she didn't feel very well. Any other man would have showed at least some small amount of concern, and complied with her request to be taken back to the club room.

The seat was against a baobab tree, and shaded by its branches. It never dawned on Jill that it was a secluded, intimate place to sit until, ten minutes after she and Patrick had made for it and settled down comfortably against the trunk of the tree, Dean and his companion strolled past, and Dean, even in the dim light, could be seen to have a half-sneer on his lips.

He looked straight at her and walked on, saying something to Sylvia which brought forth the response,

'How very kind of you, Dean. I shall love to come and dine with you.'

A week passed uneventfully after the club dance and Jill tried to fall back into the serenity of that period before Dean Lester had begun to intrude so regularly into her thoughts. She worked hard, harrowing, and cleaning out the dairy and other buildings; she bought plants for the garden and shrubs in fibre, potted and ready to put into the border she was making. Bob stood one day watching her as she did the planting.

'It's going to look very pretty,' he commented when in answer to his questions she told him how she had arranged the colours. As a matter of fact, the Fenwicks had planted a similar border of shrubs, arranging contrasts of colour to the most attractive advantage possible. This border now flourished in the garden that belonged to Dean Lester who had added to it both in length and width. 'It'll take a year or two to get established, though.'

Jill nodded, but went on to say that most of the bushes would flower from the spring onwards.

It so happened that Bob mentioned this border to Dean the next time he came over to Bangali Farm and, thinking that it was Bob's idea, he offered some cuttings of several rare shrubs.

'I've potted them and they've struck,' he went on to say, just as Jill entered the room where the men were chatting. She started, and her glance clearly said that had she known Dean was there she would have kept away. His mouth went tight, but only fleetingly. With a small lift of his shoulder that was a gesture of indifference he continued with what he was saying to her brother. 'They're healthy little plants and should do well if you put them in now.'

'Thanks a lot, Dean. But it's Jill who's making the border. She's always loved the one at Nyala Mount.'

Jill and Dean exchanged glances. He said coolly,

'I've been telling Bob that I have some rare shrubs which will go very well in your border.' His slanting sardonic glance was a question. Before she could say anything the house-boy appeared to tell Bob his presence was required outside and, excusing himself – and all unconscious of the tense atmosphere he was leaving behind – he went out. 'Well . . .?' The question was put into words. 'Do you accept the plants or don't you?' Firm taut mouth and a glinting expression. His jaw was set in a hard line and Jill had the impression that nothing would have given him greater satisfaction than to shake her. 'I saw that chin lift just now . . . but you bit back whatever you intended saying, because Bob was there—'

'You're wrong. I didn't bite back anything.'

'I won't stand here and argue with you. If you want the plants say so.'

'I'd very much like to have them,' she murmured at once, hoping she had surprised him. 'And thank you for offering them.'

Dean looked coolly at her.

'I wouldn't have offered them had I known it was you who was making the border. I offered them to Bob.'

She coloured and said, unhappily,

'I suppose I've asked for this.' He said nothing and she added, 'I'm sorry, Dean, for seeming to be ungrateful when you saved my life—'

'Don't let's be melodramatic,' he cut in with some impatience. 'If I hadn't found you someone else would

66

have done so.'

But she was shaking her head.

'I very much doubt it. I was feeling so weak by that time that I'd not have been able to hold up much longer. And once I'd become unable to call or to move about—' She broke off, spreading her hands. 'That would have been it.'

He was frowning, and thoughtful, but his gaze was fixed on hers.

'I'll send one of my boys over with the plants tomorrow,' he said, his eyes going to the window. Bob was out there and Dean added curtly that he would have to leave as he was exceedingly busy. The next moment he was chatting to Bob, and it was over an hour before he left. So he hadn't been in a hurry at all.

'Only in a hurry to get away from me,' she whispered miserably, watching the low white car sweep smoothly along the path towards the gate.

'We're invited to a sundowner tomorrow evening,' Bob informed her a few minutes later, Jill having joined him outside. 'Are you coming?' he asked, casting her an odd glance.

Automatically she shook her head. It was time, she decided, to give Bob some explanation.

'Dean and I don't get along very well. That's the reason why I always refuse his invitations.' She turned as Lucie came from the house, flushed from her task of baking bread in the big old-fashioned stove.

'I knew this,' he admitted. 'It's been clear for some time.' He looked anxiously at her. 'He's not the sort to make an unwelcome pass at you – so would you care to tell us what's happened?' He was very clearly upset, and so was Lucie as she looked inquiringly at her sister-in-law. She had caught both Jill's words and those of Bob, and although it was unlike her to display curiosity it was plain that she would be happier if there was some explanation forthcoming.

'We haven't got on right from the first,' began Jill. 'It's just one of those things. There are certain people you meet whom you can't take to.'

'I see.' Bob glanced at his wife. 'You mean,' he continued, 'that the dislike is all on your side?'

'No – no, it's mutual.'

'You spoke as if you yourself hadn't been able to take to Dean?'

'Did I?' she floundered. 'Well, I didn't mean to. As I've said, the dislike's mutual.'

'Now, perhaps ...' A long and puzzling hesitation and then Bob added, 'I'm sure it wasn't mutual at first, Jill—' Breaking off, he cast another glance at his wife. She seemed to incline her head, almost imperceptively, and Bob took it as a gesture that he could continue. 'Dean spoke most flatteringly of you immediately after I'd introduced you. But then, very soon afterwards, he had lost interest. Did you do or say anything to annoy him?'

'He spoke flatteringly?' A strange little ache of regret suddenly made itself felt. 'I didn't realize that.'

'You wouldn't,' put in Lucie. 'It was to Bob and me that he spoke about you.' She was looking at Jill's hands. They were clenched so hard that the knuckles shone through the sun-bronzed skin. 'At the time we were very gratified, because Dean was not the sort of man to indulge in light and meaningless flattery. He said you were very beautiful . . . and he hoped to get to know you better very soon.'

Jill's heart seemed to contract, as well it might, since she saw at once that Dean must have been more than a little attracted to her to say anything like that to Bob and Lucie, for he wasn't the sort of man to flatter lightly, as Lucie had just said. And now, thought Jill almost in tears, she had lost him for ever. Why hadn't she become aware of her feelings sooner? But she had been too busy disliking him, and snubbing him – and even wishing he had fallen in the river! And even when he had organized a search for her, and himself made his timely appearance to end the nightmare of fear and despair, she had failed to show her gratitude. No wonder he had no time for her now. He must be thoroughly disgusted with her, and even if he still considered her beautiful, he must be quite convinced that her beauty was only skin deep. Looking back, Jill saw that her treatment of him was unpardonable right from the start and it was a miracle that he hadn't dismissed her instantly from his thoughts. He had not, though, and now Jill realized just how much he had persevered, especially on the evening when she and her brother and sister-in-law had dined with him. He had turned back after starting off for a walk with his other two guests; he had been more than willing to indulge in pleasant conversation with her, out there, on the stoep, with the warm balmy air all around, filled with perfumes from the garden, a garden bathed in starlight. No more romantic setting could have been found . . . and she had thrown away her chances of the more intimate relationship which she now felt sure could have resulted if only she had put forth the slightest sign of encouragement on that particular occasion.

But all was now lost, and she could only try to forget him.

'I suppose,' she murmured when suddenly she realized that her companions were waiting for some comment from her, 'that there were initial misunderstandings.'

Her brother said,

'But you prefer not to talk about them?'

She bit her lip. It was so seldom that Bob and Lucie evinced undue curiosity and she felt that on this occasion she ought to satisfy them by proffering an explanation.

'It was all my fault,' she admitted frankly at length. 'I don't know why it was, but I took an instant dislike to him. That was no excuse for my being rude and unfriendly, though, nor for my not showing more gratitude when he found me – out there in the bush.' Unhappily she shook her head. 'I'd do anything to turn the clock back,' she ended, tears on her lashes.

Bob and Lucie looked at one another, Lucie giving a deep sigh.

'I can't think why you took this dislike to him,' she was forced to say at last, and it was the first time Jill had ever heard censure in her voice. 'We thought him most charming, and were in fact relieved indeed to find we had such a nice neighbour to take the place of the Fenwicks.'

'I can't explain,' returned Jill miserably, and with a shrug Bob turned and went over to the dairy. Lucie said she must go and see to her bread and Jill was left on her own, feeling so unhappy that the idea of leaving Bangali Farm and returning to England actually crept into her mind.

And the idea was to come again very soon – the following evening, in fact, for she decided at the last moment to accompany Bob and Lucie to Nyala Mount for a sundowner. What made her change her mind she would never know, but she was to regret it immediately on her arrival. For not only did Dean raise an eyebrow, in a haughty and rather annoyed sort of way, but Sylvia de Courcy also looked with faint resentment at Jill, as if she too would much have preferred her to keep away.

'You two have met,' with indifference from Dean as he glanced fleetingly at Jill before returning his gaze to Sylvia – and keeping it there for a while. 'Bob and Lucie . . . you also have met Sylvia.'

'That's right.' Bob sat down next to her. Jill and Lucie sat together on a rattan sofa and watched Dean pour the drinks. When he sat down it was on the other side of Sylvia. Where was her uncle? Jill wondered, feeling that he at least should have accompanied her to Nyala Mount even if the Drakes had not done so. It would seem that Dean had gone for her himself in the car, mused Jill, and if this were the case then the girl would surely be staying for dinner. This did prove to be the case, but they were going to town to dine, at the club.

Conversation flowed, with Sylvia contributing in her soft silvery tones, and fluttering glances at Dean practically all the time. He was obviously enjoying her company, and his face softened every time he looked her way, which was often. For Jill he had no interest what-

71

soever; she might not have been there at all and she made a vow that she would never, never come to Nyala Mount again as long as she lived.

Just before they were to leave Bob asked Dean's advice about some grafting and Dean offered to show him some he had done that very day. Lucie seemed to follow automatically, but of course Jill stayed where she was, and found herself alone on the stoep with Sylvia who had also stayed behind.

Silence, awkward and long, fell between the two until, unable to bear it any longer, Jill said, forcing a smile,

'Are you liking it at the Drakes?'

'I love it—' But the words broke as a sigh escaped the girl. 'I – I suppose you know about – about my broken engagement? Everybody does – but in a place like this one can expect news to travel, can't one?'

Jill nodded.

'We did hear about it,' she murmured, wondering why she should have so little compassion for the girl. 'It must have been very upsetting.' She did not know what to say and wished the girl hadn't brought up so intimate a subject.

'It was devastating. I thought I'd never get over it . . .' Her silvery voice trailed away as her eyes sought and found Dean's dim figure among the trees on the far side of the garden. 'But one does get over things,' she added as if to herself, and a serene smile touched the full red lips. 'Dean is so very good to me. He's been over several times and taken me out to dine. We're going to the club tonight – but he mentioned it earlier, if you remember?'

'Yes.' Jill followed the direction of her gaze; Dean

was shining a powerful torch on to one of the trees where the grafting had been done.

'I never expected to find anyone quite like him out here, in this wild place.'

'Wild?'

'Well . . . it's primitive, you must agree?'

Jill said nothing for the moment. Her gaze was on the distant kopje, its summit melting into the misty purple evening light. Often she would climb it to watch the sunset, her mind conditioned to so great a depth of appreciation that she actually felt a thrill of pleasure that was almost physical. She would find herself spell-bound as the ever-changing display of colour endowed the bushveld with a poignant, mysterious beauty sur-passing anything she had ever seen, or would see again. She would stand in awe and marvel at the genius of nature, glad she was here, so close to the fundamentals of life, and so very far away from the trivialities which man in his restlessness had thought fit to introduce, complicating his life in the process. All Jill had ever wanted, after those first few unquiet months, was to remain in Africa for the rest of her life. But now . . . Automatically her eyes found the tall arresting figure of Dean again, then sought the girl in whom he had become so keenly interested. Now . . . Jill felt she must eventually be driven to leaving the land she had so soon come to love, for life would be impossible should Sylvia become Dean's wife – or should any other woman become his wife for that matter.

'It is primitive.' The words left Jill's lips only after Sylvia had made a little prompting sound by clearing her throat. 'But it's a fascinating country; I love it.'

'You don't mind living just with your brother and his wife? I mean, don't you have any ambition to get married?'

Jill hesitated, and quite unconsciously she slid her gaze to Dean again.

'I suppose every woman wants to get married,' she replied with honesty, then added, 'But if it's your fate not to be fortunate enough to find the right man then you have to accept that you're going to be a spinster all your life.'

'I can't ever resign myself to spinsterhood. For one thing, I'm the rather helpless type of woman who needs a man's protection. For another, I should hate not to have the prestige that marriage bestows on a woman.'

Jill looked at her. This was a strange way for a broken-hearted girl to talk. Jill knew that had she herself been thrown over it would have taken her years to recover.

'These days a woman doesn't suffer loss of prestige because she's single. In fact,' added Jill without any idea that her words might ever be repeated, 'many married women envy the single ones, because they are free to do as they like. When you're married you have a great deal of conforming to do – more so if you happen to have one of those masterful men whose wives have no say in anything, who, in fact, are forced to subordinate their own wills to those of their husbands.'

Sylvia's curving dark eyebrows were raised.

'You appear to prefer the single life – the free life?'

'I did say that every woman wants to get married,' Jill gently reminded her, wondering just how this conversation had started in the first place.

'But you also said that married women envy the single ones their freedom?'

A small frown touched Jill's high forehead. She considered the topic rather silly, this inane exchange of words profitless.

'I said some married women—'

'You said many married women.'

Jill lapsed into silence, wishing more than ever that she had declined Dean's offer, as was her custom.

She looked up as he and Bob and Lucie began strolling towards the stoep, and stood up before they reached it.

'You're going now?' she asked Bob, and he nodded.

'Miss Sharman and I have been having a most pleasant conversation,' purred Sylvia with a delectable smile for Dean. 'We've been talking about marriage.'

'Indeed?' with a slant of one eyebrow and an inscrutable glance in Jill's direction.

'Miss Sharman has the most interesting views on marriage. She deplores having to conform to the requirements of another person, and considers single women more fortunate because they retain their freedom.' The smile reappeared and the big violet eyes met Dean's across the space between the stoep and the arc of light where the group was standing. Jill had gasped, but inwardly, incredulous that the girl should have repeated her words in this deliberately distorted form. Dean's mouth curved in a half-sneer as he looked at Jill.

'In that case,' he said brusquely, 'she should stay single.'

Flushing, more with anger than anything else, Jill

opened her mouth to correct what Sylvia had said, but on noticing the deep anxiety and puzzlement on the faces of Bob and Lucie, she held back what she was about to say.

'Well,' began Bob awkwardly, 'we'll be getting off. You'll be over some time in the week?'

'Yes – about Thursday or Friday.' Fleetingly Dean's eyes met those of Jill before he turned to Lucie. 'I'll send Kimani over in the morning to do that little job for you. Give him anything else you've got. He'll enjoy himself.'

'Thanks a lot, Dean. It's kind of you to bother about the job at all.'

'It's no bother. I don't need Kimani, so you might as well have him. He's a very good joiner, so don't be afraid to give him anything you want doing.'

Lucie nodded.

'The important thing at the moment is the cupboard in the kitchen. But later – if I can pay you – I'd like Kimani to build us some fitted furniture in the bedroom.'

'Is that what you want? I'll come over and advise. And I can get you the wood at a reduced price.'

'You can? Thanks again. But as I said, I must pay—'

'We'll not trouble ourselves about that, Lucie. If Kimani wasn't working for you he'd be having to find work, and he hates that.'

Lucie opened her mouth to repeat that she must pay, but she closed it again, deciding that this was not the time to begin an argument.

Final good nights were said and they were on their

way home. A rather cool silence pervaded the station wagon and Jill sensed a chill between herself and these two that would never have seemed possible. Almost from the first they had been a close-knit trio, with love and comradeship and the desire to make a prosperous business of the farm all contributing to an atmosphere of total harmony between the three of them. But now something had crept in, threatening this harmony, and Jill accepted that the blame for this was entirely hers. Dean *was* a good neighbour to replace the Fenwicks, as Lucie had maintained. He proffered help without hesitation when it was required; he never gave a party or invited friends over for a sundowner without including those from Bangali Farm in that invitation.

Her unhappy thoughts intruded long after she had gone to bed, and sleep was denied her. Should she make another attempt to repair the damage she had done? The idea of making a humble apology to Dean was far from attractive, and yet this was the only way of breaking through the barrier existing between Dean and herself.

She managed to doze at last, and the final hazy thought was a resolution. She would make a special journey to Nyala Mount in the morning, she decided, quite forgetting that only a few hours ago she had resolved never to enter Dean's house again.

CHAPTER FIVE

SHE went off after breakfast, riding Jacky, and as it was her day off anyway, there were no inquiries as to where she was going. She often went off with a packed lunch and in order to avoid any puzzlement on the part of Lucie or Bob, Jill took her sandwiches and flask as usual.

As she approached the long avenue of trees leading up to the white-gabled mansion Jill became aware of an uneasy fluttering of her nerves. It was natural, she told herself, because of the distasteful task in front of her. She had always possessed her fair share of pride, and to lower it was always hard. It would be harder still to lower it before Dean. However, her resolve remained strong and eventually she was lifting the heavy knocker on the front door. Dean himself opened it; he was dressed in a tropical suit, ready to go out, she realized with a little sinking of her heart.

'You . . .?' Not a very propitious beginning, she thought, feeling her colour rise a little. 'Is something wrong over at the farm?'

She swallowed the saliva on her tongue and said, looking up into those piercing grey eyes,

'No, Dean – b-but I myself wanted to – to talk to you.' Her eyes flickered to his immaculate attire. 'You're going out?'

He nodded, frowning at her in some puzzlement.

'In a few minutes.' He stepped aside and swept an

invitation with his hand. 'Come in.'

'Thank you.' She turned her head. 'Jacky will be all right there, tethered to that tree?'

'I should think so,' coolly and in tones indicative of faint derision that she should ask so unnecessary a question. 'Well?' he asked once they were inside, in the cool air-conditioned living-room with its tasteful and expensive furniture and long attractive drapes. 'To what do I owe the honour of a visit from you at this time of the morning?' His arrogant tone and air of half-impatient inquiry not only put her off balance but also provoked an anger which she was already having difficulty in keeping under.

'It's about you and me,' she began with difficulty. 'My brother and sister-in-law have noticed the animosity that has grown up between us, and they're troubled about it.'

The grey eyes were narrowed, fixed on her flushed face in an expression of contempt.

'And so, for your own peace of mind, you've come to ask me to indulge in a pretence, is that it?'

She averted her head, for otherwise she must surely have flashed him a glance that would have ruined her chances for ever.

'I came to apologize for — for being unfriendly towards you.'

Silence, lasting for a most uncomfortable moment.

'Well?' was all he said when at last he decided to speak.

She looked up, moistening her lips.

'I'm sorry,' she murmured in a small and quivering voice. 'I do realize that it's been all my fault.'

'I accept your apology,' he said, but in a tone devoid of warmth. 'And now?'

Jill moved uncomfortably, anger and humiliation all mixed up with the awareness of the fact that she cared for Dean, and emerging from the miscellany came the question: how had she come to care for him at all? That he had many saving graces she had already owned, but his arrogance was inherent, his high opinion of himself most firmly rooted. Surely marriage with such a man would be far from pleasant; he would make sure his wife was kept in her place, ever conscious of her husband's superiority.

'Now,' she began eventually, 'I hoped we could act in a more neighbourly manner – just for appearances' sake.' She raised her soft brown eyes to his hard grey ones and added in the same low tones, 'Bob and Lucie are troubled about the growing antagonism, because they themselves like you so much.'

'I was correct in assuming your chief concern is your own peace of mind?'

She bit her lip, having to admit that this was so.

'Only partly,' she told him. 'I hate my brother and his wife being unhappy.'

His eyes flickered over her; she became acutely aware of her unruly hair – and she thought of Sylvia de Courcy's groomed and attractive appearance.

'To imply that they're unhappy is an exaggeration, surely?'

'Perhaps,' she conceded. 'But they're troubled. They probably feel that you'll become distant with them, because of me.'

'When they know me better they'll not worry about

anything like that.' Dean glanced at his watch and his manner became hurried. 'I'm afraid I must ask you to leave; I have an appointment to keep.'

She made no immediate move to leave the room.

'You will put their minds at ease?'

'You're asking me to adopt a friendly attitude towards you?'

'I'd be grateful if you would.' She had humbled herself to the limit; if he should prevaricate any longer she felt she must surely abandon the idea of creating a friendly relationship with him and go off with her head in the air.

'I'll think about it,' was all he said, and now she had no option than to leave, since he was at the door, holding it open with one hand and with the other indicating his desire that she should go.

She rode Jacky along the river bank hoping the tranquillity would restore her composure, for she was hot inside, and half regretting the impulse that urged her to make the approach which, to say the least, had not produced the result for which she had hoped.

A small tributary which she had noticed before looked more enticing today than usual and she turned Jacky along its bank, and after about ten minutes or so she gave a little gasp and dismounted, tethering the gelding to an acacia tree and then proceeding to cross the stream by using the trunk of a fallen tree as a bridge. What had caught her attention from the other side was now a veritable botanical garden of mosses and small yellow flowers with petals like crinkled tissue paper. Tiny blue butterflies flitted among them, or hovered in mid-air. Many other flowers added hues in the full range from ochre to pearl, while epiphytic life was apparent everywhere, almost every tree supporting other forms of forest life – ferns and orchids mainly, these latter flaunting the most brilliant colours, their aerial roots gripping the trees in an endeavour to reach the sunlight.

Boulders of all shapes and sizes lay in and alongside the youthful stream and, finding one which had not been covered by moss, Jill sat down, listening to the gurgle of the water as it danced over the hard bands of rock in its ungraded bed. Here indeed was another fairyland of peace and colour and nature's wonderment. What colours! What splendour of design! How inferior were man's efforts beside the work of nature. Jill fell to wondering if anyone anywhere around knew of this haven of tranquillity; she hoped it was hers alone.

Her thoughts flitting about here and there, she would see a picture of her father, grey-haired and a little thin on top. She saw her mother, small and homely and often sighing for the things that had gone for ever with the changing years. A little old lady came into the picture: a neighbour, widowed and crying bitterly when, after the death of her father, Jill had informed her that she was leaving the house, going to make her home with Bob and Lucie in the Transvaal. She would have no one, Mrs. Pointon had said. She would now be all alone. Jill too had cried a little; the old lady would no doubt have to enter a home for the aged eventually, since none of the neighbours had been as concerned with her as Jill and her father. Mrs. Pointon's shopping had been done on a Saturday afternoon along with theirs; her soiled linen had gone into Jill's washing machine every Sunday morning, her lawn being cut at the same time by Jill's father. Sunday lunch was passed over the garden hedge by Jill – roast beef and vegetables daintily set out between two large dinner plates. In return Mrs. Pointon would take in parcels from the postman, and the bread from the roundsman who came three times a week, during the hours Jill and her father were out at work.

Mrs. Pointon had also given Jill some pretty items of jewellery on her birthdays and at Christmas. She had been comfortably off in her younger days and she still had some very beautiful things in her home.

Jill's musings were cut by the appearance of a small dainty buck timidly emerging from among the thick undergrowth on the opposite side of the stream. Its eyes, limpid and catching the shafts of sunlight penetrating the vegetation, moved alertly. Jacky happened to choose this moment to whinny and the buck shot away into the safety of the scrub.

After partaking of her sandwiches and coffee Jill decided to return to the farm. Today was spoiled, somehow, she admitted, and this was owing to the interview she'd had with their neighbour. If only he had softened, said spontaneously that he was prepared to let bygones be bygones, she would undoubtedly have left him with a lighter heart, and with her customary eager anticipation of the enjoyment of her free day.

Lucie was washing; she looked up in surprise at seeing Jill back so soon.

'I expected you to be out for hours yet?' She threw Jill a questioning glance and Jill told her she had been exploring as usual. 'But it didn't take you as long as it normally does?'

'No; I felt restless, somehow.' Her big brown eyes met the blue ones and smiled. 'I think I'll go to town. I need some writing-paper and envelopes, and one or two other items.'

'Oh – well, in that case, you can bring me some screws.'

'Screws?'

'Kimani wants them. I've got the size and number on a piece of paper.'

Jill took a bath and washed her hair. It shone and the sun-bleached part at the front looked particularly attractive, but she sighed for all that, and frowned as she endeavoured to flatten down those insistent ends that flicked up, especially those of her fringe. It was useless and she tossed the hairbrush down with a small grunt of disgust. She wore a perpetual wind-teased look and always had, ever since she could remember. One day, she thought, she'd plunge and buy a wig!

A newly-laundered, crisply starched white shirt restored some of her confidence in her appearance; the tight-fitting jeans of ribbed velvet also looked attractive.

She turned before the mirror and grimaced. Women, said one famous French fashion designer, should always wear any garment one size too small. Well, either she had not been paying attention when she bought these jeans, or else life in South Africa had rounded her a little!

Nevertheless, she rather liked the finished product, once she had put on her narrow belt and broad-brimmed hat.

'Countrified but very charming,' was Bob's comment, and both Jill and Lucie laughed.

'I don't think I'll ever look anything else but countrified,' pronounced Jill, and although her mind did at
this moment flit to her idea of leaving here, she knew
that, deep down, the wrench would be too great once the
time for it arrived. Her spirits seemed to have lightened
enormously during the past couple of hours and she felt
she would be able to crush her feelings for Dean in time.
After all, it wasn't as if they had ever experienced one
intimate moment together, so really there were no mem-
ories to intrude, and to cause pain. Yes, she would put
up a resistance. Her life at Bangali Farm had been idyl-
lic until the coming of Dean Lester, and Jill determined
to recapture what she had lost.

She drove to town in the station wagon, humming a
little tune to herself as she bumped along on the rough
track before reaching the wider, smoother main road
into Breysburg. On her arrival she parked the car and
gave Patrick a ring. He was eager to join her for afternoon tea and arranged to meet her at the café at half past
three. Meanwhile, Jill did all her shopping and then
strolled round the park.

At half past three she was at the café. Patrick had just
arrived, breezy as ever and declaring they would have
tea at the club, and not at the café after all.

'But it'll be too expensive,' protested Jill, who always
insisted on paying for herself when she and Patrick ate
together.

'I've had a win on the horses! My treat, Jill girl, and
no arguments.'

'In that case,' she agreed, 'we'll go to the club.'

Patrick took her in his car, Jill having left her vehicle

where she had first parked it, and walked to the café.

'Here we are.' Patrick made for a space between two cars just as another driver had the same idea. 'Too late, old man—' he began, when he realized who it was. Jill went hot, for Patrick's action was inordinately bad-mannered, the low white car having been there first, and the driver already manoeuvring it with the intention of backing into the space. Patrick had swept in, nose first, and Dean was now left to find another place. This he did; Jill watched him slide from the car, cast a glance of cool contempt at Patrick, then open the other door to allow his companion to get out. His hand tucked itself under her elbow as, daintily, Sylvia put a white-shod foot to the ground and, taking advantage of the support offered, made a regal exit from the car. She was dressed in a blue and white linen suit, with white handbag and a wide-brimmed straw hat. She and Dean certainly looked a well-matched couple, Jill reluctantly admitted, swallowing to release the sudden dryness in her throat. Dean nodded to her, his keen eyes taking in her apparel – the very tight-fitting jeans and white cotton shirt, open at the neck to reveal a sun-tanned throat. And then his glance went to the girl at his side, and Jill squirmed inwardly as she sensed the comparison that was being made.

Turning towards the terrace on which tea was being served, Dean and Sylvia were conducted to a table shaded by trees, right at the far end of the terrace. Jill and Patrick sat a small distance from them, Jill still profoundly conscious of the warmth which embarrassment had caused to spread through her at Patrick's action. She wished she had not bothered to telephone

86

him, but had gone straight home after completing her shopping. However, the damage was done now and there was nothing for it but to make some attempt to enjoy the light meal put before her. But naturally her eyes strayed repeatedly to the arresting couple, sitting there, in the rather intimate seclusion afforded by the trees, the boughs of which drooped in lacy formations often right down to the ground.

'They're seen about together a great deal.' Patrick's remark carried an envious ring and Jill looked curiously at him, bringing her gaze from the back of Dean's head.

'They are?'

Patrick nodded.

'They were at the polo match on Saturday.'

'I thought Dean played?'

'So he does, but he wasn't playing on Saturday. He'll use only one horse, a special one, and it's gone lame.' Jill said nothing and Patrick continued, 'They were here last evening, dining and dancing. I think every man in the place was envious of Dean Lester.'

'You were here?'

'No, but I heard all about it.' Patrick took a drink of tea and watched the couple in silence for a space. 'I wonder just how serious it is?'

Jill felt the dryness settle in her throat again. Dean and Sylvia married . . .

'Dean doesn't strike me as the marrying sort.' She just had to say this, hoping Patrick would readily agree with her, but he was shaking his head.

'At one time I'd have thought so, but not now, not since the advent of the glamorous Sylvia de Courcy. The attraction would be sufficient on its own – her beauty,' he elucidated, before adding, 'But she's been jilted; pity's another emotion which affects a man. He always wants to console a girl who's been badly treated – and more especially if she possesses the beauty of Sylvia.'

'Do you really believe that pity is playing an important part in their relationship?'

'Most certainly. I myself became conscious of pity when I heard she'd been jilted. Poor girl . . .' He was shaking his head and a frown knit his brow. 'A girl puts such faith in the man who proposes marriage; it must be shattering for her when she's cast off.'

Jill stared at him.

'For a man you appear to have an amazing insight into a woman's feelings.'

'I have imagination, and can use it.'

'Pity,' said Jill, her eyes straying once again to the couple under the trees, 'is no basis for marriage.'

'It's a basis for the beginning of love. Why, thousands of love affairs have sprung from pity.'

Jill failed to see how Patrick could be so sure of this, but she made no comment about it. Dean and Sylvia were both leaning towards one another across the table; it savoured of a most intimate scene, and one which Jill no longer desired to witness. She moved her chair a little, so that she was sitting with her back to them, and she concentrated on eating her tea.

When it was over she and Patrick strolled in the gardens for a short while before he took her back to the place where her station wagon was parked.

'See you,' he said, lifting a hand as, after seeing her into the driver's seat and closing the door, he began to move away towards his own car. Jill drove a short way and then stopped to collect any mail that might be waiting at the post office. There were two letters for Bob and, to her surprise, one for her, the postmark above the typewritten name and address being that of the town in which she and her father had worked – the nearest town to where they had lived.

So curious was she that even before reaching the station wagon again she was slitting the envelope.

'Brown, Stackland and Brown ... solicitors ...' She sat in the cab and read on. Mrs. Pointon had died ... and left everything she possessed to Jill. Stunned, she could only stare, unable to assimilate just what it meant, because her chief thought was of the old lady herself. She had died in her sleep – thank goodness – but nevertheless a deep sadness enveloped Jill. She had had a great affection for the old lady, and although she was glad in one way that she had died peaceably, in her own home which she loved, she wished she had lived a little while longer.

Bob, not having known Mrs. Pointon anywhere near as well as had Jill, was concerned only with the inheritance.

'Did she have much?' he asked, handing back the letter to Jill, who had given it to him immediately on arriving back at the farm.

'The house was hers and she had lots of lovely things – antique china and a great deal of silver.'

'Old silver?'

'Yes, I understood her to say it was old – Georgian, I think.'

'Then you're going to be well-off, it seems.'

Jill's eyes were shadowed; the conversation brought back with poignant intensity the death of her father and the rather hard-hearted way his affairs had been wound up. These things had to be done in a businesslike manner, she supposed, but her thoughts were still with the dear old lady whose gratitude had always been strong, and manifested by the lovely presents she had given Jill. When she was doing those little things for Mrs. Pointon the thought of reward such as this had never once entered her head. Mrs. Pointon had a distant relative, a cousin, who had emigrated many years ago and, had Jill ever even thought about the money – which she never had – she would have concluded that this relative would receive all that the old lady had to leave.

'The solicitors want me to go over,' she said at last, 'but I imagine they can do everything without my presence being necessary.'

Bob was thoughtful, but it was his wife who spoke.

'I'd go if I were you, Jill,' she advised. 'This silver – it could disappear, you know.'

'Disappear?' frowned Jill. 'Who could take it?'

'When my aunt died almost everything in the house had disappeared by the time we got there. All sorts of people had got into the house and helped themselves. Besides, wouldn't Mrs. Pointon want you to go over and clear the house yourself?'

A frown still creased Jill's brow.

'I don't care for the idea at all,' she began, when Bob interrupted to say that he agreed with Lucie, and that if it was at all possible he would take time off to go to England with her. At this, Jill agreed to accede to the solicitors' request and left the arrangements for their flight to her brother.

The following evening Dean was among several friends invited to a sundowner at Bangali Farm. He phoned during the afternoon to say he would be late, as he was supervising the felling of some trees and would be working until it was dark. Bob then said he might as well stay to dinner and Dean accepted the invitation.

'Dean's staying to dinner.' Bob looked at Jill as he mentioned this to Lucie. 'You can manage another?'

'Of course.' Lucie also glanced fleetingly at Jill who, colouring slightly, decided to ease the situation by changing the subject. Dean's name wasn't mentioned again until, on his arrival, Charles Goulding hailed him from the stoep where the party was sitting with their drinks. Dean leapt the steps, producing a smile for Lucie and a nod of cool indifference for Jill.

When the rest of the guests had departed and the two couples were at dinner, Bob mentioned the fact that Jill would be going to England in two days' time and that he had arranged to go with her.

'She's had some money left to her, and a house and its contents,' Bob explained. 'Jill wasn't very keen on going over, but Lucie and I felt she should. Don't you agree?'

Dean nodded his head.

'It would be best.' He looked at Jill. 'You must be feeling very happy at your good fortune?'

Automatically she shook her head.

'I was very fond of Mrs. Pointon; I'm sorry she's dead.'

'She was our neighbour,' put in Bob. 'Jill and Father

91

looked after her, as she'd no one else to do so.'

Dean was still looking across the table at Jill; she felt the chill of his prolonged unsmiling stare and glanced away. His unapproachability was beginning to hurt badly; tears were caught in a cloud behind her eyes, and despair filled her heart.

'If you want me to do anything while you're away,' Dean was saying later as they sat with their after dinner drinks on the stoep, 'just say so.'

'That's very good of you, Dean.' Bob looked gratefully at him and went on to say that Lucie would send over to Nyala Mount if any sort of emergency should arise. 'Not that we're expecting anything to happen,' he added with a grimace.

'Of course not, but one never knows. This is a cruel country and it pays to be prepared for eventualities.'

His words rang in Jill's ears when, the following day, she heard a scream come from the direction of the shed where the kerosene was kept, and, throwing down the hoe with which she had been clearing the weeds from her shrubbery, she dashed towards it, arriving in time to see Lucie stagger out and collapse at her feet.

'Lucie – what . . .?' Horror crept into her voice as, eyes dilating, she saw the puffiness at the sides of her sister-in-law's neck. 'A . . . snake?' Lucie could only nod and raise a swollen hand. 'I'll fetch Bob—' began Jill.

'He went to town . . .'

'He's out? Oh, God!' Jill cried in a stricken tone. 'What must I do?' Dean! Within seconds she was talking to him on the telephone, relief surging through her at finding him in.

92

'Please come, Dean—'

'I'll phone the hospital for serum to be fetched over; then I'll be with you. Get the boy and take her inside. Watch yourself! Do you hear?' The tone was all command but Jill fully understood his anxiety.

'I think the snake's in – in the shed.'

'Close the door before you do anything else!' He was gone. Jill called the house-boy and together they got Lucie into the house and laid her on the bed. Lucie's face was purple now and Jill felt hot perspiration sweep over her entire body as terror gripped her. Lucie – so dainty and alive, adored by her husband and dearly loved by Jill.

'The serum is being rushed over.' Dean's crisp words in her ear was the first Jill knew of his arrival. He had walked unheard into the bedroom and was now bending over the girl lying on the bed, a light blanket covering her. Watching Dean's face, while her heart raced madly and every nerve in her body rioted, Jill saw that his expression was grim.

'Is she . . .? Will she . . .?' What she wanted to say wouldn't come, prevented by the blockage in her throat. But the trapped tears did come and Jill sought vainly for a handkerchief. 'How – how long will they be?' she whispered, still looking round vaguely for something on which to dry her eyes. Dean assured her that no time would be lost.

'Here,' he said, offering her his handkerchief. 'Sit down. There's not a thing you can do.'

She shook her head.

'I can't sit down— Here they are! Thank God!' And because all the strength left her legs Jill swayed and would have fallen had not Dean caught her and put her into a chair. 'Now just stay there,' he commanded. 'Move and you'll answer to me!' He left her then and it seemed an eternity before he returned.

'Is she all right? I mean, were they in time?'

He nodded.

'She'll be all right.' His voice was brusque. He said something about catching the snake, but his words seemed a long way off. Jill's relief was almost as great a test to her nerves as her terror had been. 'You need a drink,' he said, and went over to the cupboard where she drinks were kept. The people from the hospital were still with Lucie and soft mumblings could be heard coming from her room. 'Here, drink this.'

'If it's brandy, I can't,' she began, but got no further. Dean was in no mood for argument; he put the glass to her lips with one hand and held her head firmly with the other.

'I've things to do,' he snapped. 'Drink this and don't fuss.'

She obeyed – there was nothing else she could do, with his hold on her like this and his body towering above her.

'Thank you.' She tried not to cough but failed. 'It's so strong . . .'

'You were all to pieces. You'll feel better directly.' He paused a second or two. 'I've to see about that snake – there could very possibly be more than one. I'll use your telephone,' and he strode away to where it was, in a small room which led off the small hall by an archway made of polished mahogany.

Jill shivered for a short while and then the warmth of

94

the spirit flowed through her body and she felt better. A doctor came from Lucie's room followed by a nurse carrying a leather case.

'It's your sister-in-law, I believe?' Jill nodded and he went on, 'She must be kept in bed for a couple of days. She's young and will soon recover, but it will be good for her to have the rest.'

He met Dean as he went out, still followed by the nurse. Jill heard them talking together, then the departure of the doctor and nurse was evidenced by the sound of their car starting up and crunching away towards the lane.

Dean had phoned his superintendent, who came over soon afterwards with a couple of men. They went with Dean to the shed, but although everything was brought out and thoroughly examined, the snake was not to be found.

'You mean,' faltered Jill who, having been ordered to remain indoors while the search was going on, was still sitting in the chair in which Dean had put her, 'that it'll still be somewhere around?'

'We've made a search, and my men are still beating about in the grass and bushes. I believe you've seen the last of it.'

'We've never had a snake before.' She was frightened, but Dean's unperturbed countenance went some way to reassuring her. 'I knew it was a snake bite, though, because our house-boy had told me about his mother being bitten, and he described what she looked like.' Breaking off, Jill gave a great shudder. 'I was terrified that she would – would die.'

Dean nodded understandingly. All antagonism was

gone, swept away on their mutual anxiety for Lucie.

'I'm glad you thought to get in touch with me at once.'

'So am I.' She looked up at him, gratitude in her soft brown eyes. 'I can't thank you enough, Dean. You don't know how I feel . . . I can't explain.' Her mouth quivered; she saw the slow change of his expression as the familiar taut lines began to fade, giving way to a softer but unfathomable element she had never seen before. 'I just hope you're able to understand how deeply grateful I am to you—'

'That's enough, Jill,' he broke in quietly but firmly. 'I don't want gratitude or thanks. As I've said, I'm glad you thought fit to send for me.' He looked straight at her. 'If you hadn't, I'm afraid there would have been serious consequences.' His words, spoken so very softly, conveyed all they were meant to convey and the underlying warning was not lost on her either. Had she allowed pride to rise above the urgency of the situation and stubbornly refused to contact Dean, then Lucie would have died. Also, he was telling her, should there ever be such a situation again, or any other serious eventuality, she must not fail to get into touch with him, as she had on this occasion. 'Action in any emergency must be prompt,' he was adding in the same soft firm tones. 'Remember that, Jill – and also remember that those of us who have been born here do know more about the country and its dangers than those who have come later. We're always ready and willing to help – if we're asked for help.'

She sad, rather humbly,

'I fully understand, Dean. I'll never fail to ask your

help if ever it's needed.'

'Good girl.' He glanced up as his superintendent appeared in the open window leading out to the stoep. 'Anything?'

'No. It's gone. It was just a stray; you might never see another in years.' He was looking at Jill, attempting to allay any fears she still might have. 'Snakes get out of the way of humans, mainly, miss. This one must accidentally have got into the shed, so when Mrs. Sharman went in it struck – probably because it thought it was trapped. In the ordinary way they don't strike at humans.'

Jill let out a long breath of relief.

'You must remember always to close doors,' warned Dean. 'But as Hutchinson says, you might never see another in years.'

Hutchinson retired along with the two boys who were still outside. Dean stayed until Bob appeared, which was within ten minutes of the men's departure. He listened to what had happened, his expression changing from fear to relief and finally to gratitude as he thanked both Jill and Dean for the promptness of their actions.

'Can I go in and see her?' he asked.

'Of course. We've just been with her. You'll find her suffering from shock, and a trifle scared, but she'll be all right in no time at all.' He then said he must be going, but stopped to talk to Jill a moment or two after she had walked with him out on to the stoep. 'You'll be going to England on your own, I take it?'

'I don't know. Certainly Bob can't now be expected to come with me. Perhaps I'll postpone the visit.'

'There doesn't seem any need, not to me, that is.

Your flight's all arranged, and the lawyers will be expecting you. However, it's none of my business.'

'I'll think about it,' she decided, swayed a little by his words. 'Perhaps it would be as well to get it over and done with.'

He nodded, lifted a hand, and was gone. She walked back into the living-room and watched his departure from the side window. The low white car rolled across the gravel, then out on to the path leading to the road. She felt lighter than for a long time. Nothing, she vowed, was going to impair this new relationship which had come to Dean and herself as a result of what had happened to Lucie.

And it was partly because of Dean's advice about proceeding with the trip to England that Jill decided to carry on with it. She felt that should she not go, then Dean might take it as a slight and this she did not want. The position between them was still tricky; she felt that one false move on her part would take her right back to where she was before the incident of the snake.

Both Bob and Lucie were a little concerned about her going alone, but she pointed out that she was twenty-four and perfectly able to take care of herself.

Dean rang to ask about Lucie, and Bob must have mentioned that Jill was taking the trip because when Bob came from the phone he said that Dean would take her to the airport.

'He will.' She had thought she would have to drive the station wagon, taking their head man, who could drive it back. 'That's most kind of him.'

Bob looked at her.

'You two seem to have buried the hatchet,' he commented without much expression.

'The emergency did it.'

Her brother nodded his head.

'Situations like that do usually result in all parties forgetting everything except the task in hand.' He paused a moment. 'I'm glad, Jill. As you must have known, Lucie and I were worried.'

'Yes, I realized that.' She refrained from telling him of her apology. It didn't matter anyway, not now that the atmosphere between her and Dean was cleared.

He arrived in plenty of time, took up the suitcase standing there on the stoep, and within five minutes they were on the road. It was early and dawn was streaking across the sky, painting the veld with every colour from fiery rose to palest gold.

'It's kind of you to go to all this trouble,' she began, when a sound of the half-impatient issuing of breath pulled her up. 'Thank you,' she added simply, and nothing more was said on the subject, Jill deciding to give herself up to her customary appreciation of the bushveld at sunrise. The whole landscape was a panoply of matchless beauty, a tableau of colour and magic.

'I've a flask of coffee in the car,' Dean told her presently. 'Don't go thirsty. We'll stop when you feel like a drink.'

'Thanks, Dean. I'll wait a little while – unless you want a drink now?'

He shook his head, his attention caught by a small brown deer that pranced across the road in front of the car.

'Not at the moment.'

'It's a glorious morning,' she had to say, even though

it must sound prosaic to Dean's ears. He had seen mornings like this all his life. But he nodded and agreed, and went on to point out the vivid splash of crimson behind a distant kopje. 'It's – frightening,' breathed Jill in an awed voice, and a smile touched the corners of her companion's mouth.

'I suppose it is, when you come to think about it.' A small thoughtful pause and then, 'People don't think of the sun as just a mass of gas and flame. They think of it as it's seen – nice and round and warm and light-giving.'

Jill agreed.

'Our existence depends solely on it – all life, in fact.'

'All life,' he repeated seriously, and a silence fell after that, a companionable silence which Jill knew she would always remember, for it seemed like a balm after the despair and hurt she had endured since discovering her feelings for Dean.

CHAPTER SIX

THEY stopped an hour later, by a stream, and Dean poured the coffee.

'There's extra milk in this other flask if you want it.' He handed the cup to her, his face unsoftened yet not hard in the way it had been of late. 'You look pale. Didn't you sleep?'

'Yes, I slept, but fitfully, knowing I had to be up so early.' She smiled at him, willing a response, but although a strange expression entered his eyes his mouth remained firm. 'I always go pale when I'm worried.'

'You're worried?'

'I haven't made a journey like this before.'

'Bob told me you'd lightly passed off his anxiety, saying you could take care of yourself.'

'I did. Naturally I didn't want him to be worrying about me at this time.'

Dean was frowning slightly.

'There's nothing to worry about, Jill. I'll see to everything when we get to the airport, and someone's meeting you at the other end, so Bob told me?'

'Yes, the solicitors are sending someone. I'll be all right,' she added hastily. 'But you know how it is when you're doing something for the first time. You do worry a little.'

He smiled now and said,

'I think I understand.'

'Perhaps . . .' She looked at him with an examining

stare, her coffee cup poised close to her mouth. 'But perhaps you don't,' she added inconsistently, 'being a man. I can't imagine you worrying about anything.'

'No?' He looked at her with an odd expression. 'True, I wouldn't worry myself about a journey; nevertheless, I do worry sometimes.'

The air suddenly seemed to vibrate around her. She recalled with a flash of memory that Dean had once told Bob and Lucie that he hoped to know her better very soon. The beautiful Sylvia de Courcy intruded at this point, but was instantly dismissed. This interlude belonged to Jill alone . . . and perhaps to Dean. Jill could not be sure if he too was aware of the electric currents in the air.

Jill took a long drink and held out her cup for a refill as Dean picked up the flask from the grass beside him. The sun, higher now in the sky, caught the finely-etched features at an angle, giving them a faint softness; it caught his brown hair too, and strands of bronze became revealed to Jill's eyes for the first time. How extremely attractive he was! Even the arrogant mouth and set of his broad shoulders seemed attractive to her this morning.

'You haven't any idea when you'll be back?' Dean broke the silence at last, and Jill shook her head.

'I don't know what there is to do – not properly. I have to go through Mrs. Pointon's things, take what I want and the rest will be sold—' She broke off, pain stealing over her. 'It's all so depressing,' she ended, putting the cup to her lips again.

'It is, but these things have to be done.' He poured more coffee into his own cup, his expression thoughtful, his gaze directed towards a low line of hills, silhouetted against the brittle African sky. The stream itself wound about at the foot of these hills which formed a tapestry of green as a backcloth. A small cut-off meander shone brilliantly in the sun, like a lake of quicksilver. The whole scene, spun from an interweaving of all these facets, reached the ultimate of perfection. 'It's a great pity, though, that Bob couldn't have gone with you.' Dean looked at her. 'You have friends who will be willing to help you, surely?'

'I have one or two friends, yes, but they're all working. Perhaps Linda – she was my best friend till I left England, and we've still kept in touch – will be able to come along at the week-end and help me sort out.'

'This Mrs. Pointon – she had a good deal of furniture and the like?'

'Yes, the house was cluttered—' Jill smiled faintly as recollection brought back the occasion when, Mrs. Pointon being off colour, she, Jill, would go in and do her cleaning for her. 'You know how it is with old people; they treasure everything.'

'My grandmother was like that,' he commented with a dawning smile. 'It sounds as if you're going to have a job?'

'Mrs. Pointon used to say the loft was full of stuff.'

'Then you really must get some help,' he said firmly. 'If you can't persuade your friend to help you then pay someone.' His gaze fixed hers. 'That's good advice, Jill; I hope you'll take it?'

She nodded, experiencing a glow of warmth because it was plainly evident that he was anxious about her.

'Yes, Dean, I'll take it.'

'Knowing you, you'll be depressed at spending hours and hours alone on a task such as that.' He stopped as a thought struck him. 'You must stay either with a friend or at an hotel – not alone in that house.'

It was clearly an order, although Jill did wonder if Dean himself realized this. What he had said was automatic, as the whole scene had obviously presented itself most clearly to him. He saw her there, in the house where the old lady had so recently died, employed in the unhappy task of going through possessions treasured and collected over the years both by Mrs. Pointon and her husband. Jill warmed to Dean for his understanding – but more so for his phrase 'knowing you', which revealed the fact that he had at some time or another been interested enough to study her character a little.

He was looking at his watch; soon he was putting the flasks into the car, and they were on their way again, travelling a road through the veld, shimmering already from the refracted glare of the sun which was steadily rising to its zenith.

'It's going to rain,' prophesied Dean half an hour later, and Jill glanced at him in surprise. She was used to the deluges that broke suddenly when the saturated air could no longer hold its load and the upsweep of draught brought on the cooling which caused the rain, but she saw no signs of rain at present.

'Are you sure?'

'Just wait for it,' he warned, and within minutes there was a great peal of thunder and a rattling on the roof, prelude to the downpour, a downpour so violent that Dean was forced to stop the car, the wipers becoming ineffective against water that flowed like a river in flood.

That lovely period of after-dawn was drenched, lost in the rain and the angry thunderclouds blackening the sky.

'What a change in a matter of minutes,' she sighed, but Dean was quite happy about the rain.

'This deluge will go some way to paying off the arrears,' he pronounced with satisfaction, and then he added with another glance at his wrist-watch, 'Lucky I gave us plenty of time.'

She thought, 'Yes, he would give himself plenty of time,' and now there was no denouncing of him as 'clever' but only efficient. How she had changed towards him! It seemed quite impossible that she had been for-ever finding flaws in his character, branding him pompous and self-opinionated, disliking him even to the extent of hoping he would suffer the indignity of falling in the river.

After the rain the colour effects were magnificent, with a rainbow of clear pure colours supplementing a myriad tints of rose and peach and soft translucent pearl. A glow hovered above the low-growing bushes of the veld and the end of the rainbow disappeared behind a cactus-topped kopje away in the far distance.

'It's magic,' whispered Jill to herself as the car sped on again, splashing through the rivulets coming down from the higher places on to the road.

Dean slanted her a glance.

'Magic? Is that how you see it?'

'I love Africa,' she confessed, 'in all its moods.'

'And it does have moods,' was his grim rejoinder.

'This is one of its softer moods,' she murmured, glancing up at the tall gums under which they were now passing. They lined the road on both sides, affording a lacy shade from the sun's fierce rays. Steam rose from the grasses, filling the thirsty air again. 'It's always delightful after the rain.'

Dean was now concentrating on his driving and, sensing that he no longer wished to be engaged in conversation Jill also lapsed into silence, and this continued for the rest of the journey.

Dean saw to everything at the airport, and it was only when she was aboard the plane and taking off that she remembered she had forgotten to say a final thank you. But, somehow, she knew he would understand – and he wouldn't want her to become effusively grateful anyway. Already he had given her to understand this.

Jill's friend had not hesitated to assist, meeting Jill at Mrs. Pointon's house early on the morning after she had telephoned her the previous night.

'How lucky that I'm on holiday,' said Linda, clearly happy at her friend's good fortune and at seeing her again. 'I couldn't believe it when you phoned. And after we'd rung off Mum said I ought to ask you to stay with us, but of course I hadn't a number to ring you back. Where did you stay?' Jill told her the name of the hotel and heard Linda declare that she must collect her bag and move in with her. 'Mum said definitely I must bring you back with me.'

'Thank you very much, Linda. I do feel so much better now. I was certainly not looking forward to performing this task alone, I can tell you. And as for staying at an hotel – that's rather depressing too. You feel so lost when you're on your own.'

'I can well imagine it.' Linda made a swift survey of the room in which she and Jill were standing. It was the living-room, but there were two further downstairs rooms excluding the hall. 'How many bedrooms? Same as you had?'

'No; Mrs. Pointon's house is different from ours. She has four bedrooms.' It never struck Jill that she was speaking as though the old lady were still alive. 'And they're all fully furnished. Where on earth must we start?'

'Well, I suggest we empty one of these rooms completely – stuffing everything into the others— Yes, I know it seems an impossibility, but we will manage it. This leaves us with the empty room in which to put those articles which you want to keep. The removal men will then make no mistakes.'

'That's a very good idea,' agreed Jill, trying all the time to throw off the dejection which she felt at coming into the house she had known so well, and finding it so lost and empty despite the masses of furniture and bric-à-brac which abounded everywhere.

The two girls worked on for the whole of the day, Jill running out at lunch time to the shop on the corner for sandwiches and cakes, and trying desperately to get away as quickly as she could, but failing as Mrs. Mansfield, the owner, kept plying her with questions. That her inheritance was the talk of the neighbourhood was clearly evident, thought Jill with a grimace.

She'd made a pot of tea, Linda said when Jill at last returned, apologizing for being away so long.

'Mrs. Mansfield hasn't changed a bit! It's a wonder her throat doesn't ache!'

'Talks a lot? These corner-shop owners always do. Bet she wanted to know all about your good fortune?'

'And about Africa. She seemed to think I lived among man-eating savages!'

Linda gave a laugh and took the various paper bags which Jill had placed on the kitchen table.

'What have we? Ah, salmon sandwiches. She sells them? I wouldn't have thought so.' Linda was putting them out on to a plate, while Jill took crockery from the cupboard.

'There's a small sewing factory in the next road. The girls buy sandwiches from her every day.'

'Oh, I see. Gosh, I'm hungry!'

'So am I.'

The afternoon sped just as swiftly as the morning and at last the two girls had to stop working.

'I'll get a taxi to the hotel,' Jill said, and went to the phone which, fortunately, had not been disconnected.

'I'll come with you,' offered Linda, 'then we'll go straight home in the same taxi.'

Mrs. Mason, Linda's mother, greeted Jill enthusiastically, giving her a little hug and a kiss on the cheek.

'How very nice to see you, dear. I was so sorry, last night, that we couldn't ring you back. Had we known the name of your hotel we most certainly would have phoned and asked you to come here. However, you're here now, and there's a nice hot meal ready when you are. Perhaps you'd like to go to your room first. And you know where the bathroom is . . .' She tailed off, eyes twinkling as she caught her daughter's amused glance. 'Be off with you, Linda! I haven't seen Jill for a long while, so I shall talk if I want!'

Laughing, the two friends left the room together and went upstairs to their respective bedrooms, Jill taking her suitcase with her. This, she decided, was far preferable to staying in the hotel. She was a home bird, her father had always maintained, and this was true. Jill had discovered it more than ever since moving to her brother's farm, for she wanted nothing more than to potter about the house and garden, or do some rather more strenuous work in the maize fields. She liked the outings to the club; and the various invitations which she received were accepted with pleasurable anticipation for the most part, a pleasant evening being almost always assured, but any more glamorous form of entertainment was not in Jill's line at all.

'Use the bathroom first,' called Linda from across the landing. 'If you're anything like me you must be feeling grubby, to say the least.'

'It was grubby work.' Leaving her unpacking, Jill grabbed the clean towel put there on a chair for her and went along to the bathroom. A good wash made her feel better and she looked spick and span when half an hour later she entered the small dining-room from where there came a delicious smell of casseroled steak.

Mr. Mason had come in and was ready to sit down. He smiled and shook hands with Jill, politely asking about Africa and then going on to mention her inheritance.

'You kept in touch with the old lady, apparently?' he said.

'Yes. We wrote to one another regularly. But I never for one moment thought she intended leaving me all her possessions.'

'She didn't ever give you a clue?'

'Not once.'

'Well, you must have been kind to her, Jill, so you deserve to be rewarded.'

Jill said nothing; she would have preferred to know that Mrs. Pointon was still alive, but as this was a futile wish she naturally made no mention of it.

'Linda's just been saying that it's going to take a long time – the sorting-out, I mean?' Mrs. Mason bustled in carrying a loaded tray which she put down on the sideboard. 'It's a good thing Linda has a full week off work.'

'Oh, but I couldn't let her help me for that long,' protested Jill, glancing at her friend who, having followed her mother from the kitchen, now began helping her to put out the meat and vegetables on the plates.

'I love doing it,' she declared. 'What else would I be doing if it wasn't that?'

'Well . . . you could be having a rest.'

'And become bored?' Linda shook her head. 'If I'd had any money I'd have gone away, but as I haven't any money I've had to stay at home. So this is really a diversion, more pleasant for me than for you, obviously.'

Jill gave a small, deprecating shrug.

'I'm fully aware of the fact that I'm fortunate in inheriting such beautiful things. It's just that I feel so sad. You see, Mrs. Pointon was so sweet, and rather frail, though by no means helpless. Mainly, she managed to do for herself, except when she had a cold, or was off colour in some other way.'

'I seem to remember that you always did her laundry

for her,' commented Mrs. Mason, putting a well-filled plate before her husband.

'It wasn't any trouble at all; it went in with ours. She didn't have a washing-machine, you see. She was afraid of them.'

'Apparently she could well have afforded to send her washing out.' This from Linda who many times during the day had given gasps of appreciation at some of the lovely things that had passed through her hands. Particularly attractive to her had been the ivory fan which – so Mrs. Pointon had always maintained – had been given to one of Mary Queen of Scots' ladies in waiting when the unfortunate queen stood on the scaffold. How it had come into Mrs. Pointon's hands Jill had never found out, but she liked to think that the story was true. Linda certainly did, and Jill was seriously considering making her a gift of the fan, feeling sure that Mrs. Pointon would not have minded in the least, since it was going to a most appreciative owner.

'Yes, she could afford to send her washing out, but she hated the idea of its being put with so many other people's.' Jill took up her napkin and spread it on her lap as her dinner was placed on the table. 'She didn't mind its being washed with ours, she said, because she knew us.'

'She sounds funny, and rather sweet, and old-fashioned.'

Jill nodded.

'She was all those things. Father and I thought the world of her. It was a wrench when the split came.'

After dinner they sat chatting, and at half past eight Mr. Mason offered to take them to a country inn and buy them a drink.

'Lovely!' exclaimed Linda. 'Jill will enjoy the atmosphere at the Abbey Royal. Let's go there.'

Mr. and Mrs. Mason exchanged glances. The Abbey Royal was just about the most expensive country club in the whole of the county. People came from far and wide to dine there, and to dance and drink. Floor shows, put on every Saturday night, were also considered the best in the county. However, Mr. Mason agreed and the four were driven out into the country, Mr. Mason at the wheel of his big, comfortable Rover car.

The lounge of the Abbey Royal just dripped luxury with its expensive, tasteful furniture, carpets and fittings. A glittering bar stood at one end; dazzling chandeliers hung above and around it and soft classical music issued from somewhere behind it, being relayed through small inconspicuous speakers in various other parts of the great, high-domed room that, owing to its unadorned red sandstone walls and arches, gave evidence of having been part of the original monastery. Many additions had been made, of course, such as the ballroom and the long low dining-room so often used for weddings and other functions.

Wealth seemed everywhere; Jill was fascinated by the woman behind the bar. The only female, she looked more like a queen than anything else.

'She's got more edge on her than Lady Thingummy over there,' laughed Linda, watching Jill's fixed stare.

'Lady—? She's a titled lady?'

'Yes – and a millionairess.' Linda's brow furrowed. 'Dad, what's her name? It's a peculiar one; I never can remember it?'

'No, neither can I . . . yet it's on the tip of my tongue—Look,' he suddenly digressed, 'isn't that young Dawson? His father's just bought another block of flats.'

Linda looked and said yes, it was George Dawson. He was drinking at the bar with another young man and as Linda looked George Dawson caught her eye and, turning to say something to his companion, he led the way towards the table at which the four were sitting.

'Hello, Linda! Mr. and Mrs. Mason!' George Dawson eyed Jill, who murmured 'How do you do' as Linda made the introductions.

'Are you sitting down?' Mr. Mason moved his chair. George was saying,

'Meet Clark . . .' More introductions and a rearranging of chairs. Clark muttered something about having left his drink on the counter and disappeared for a moment.

'Be nice to him,' said George urgently when the handsome young man was out of earshot. 'He's just about as low as can be. His fiancée's vanished into thin air.'

'Vanished?' echoed Mrs. Mason. 'How can that be?'

'It's the biggest mystery—' He spread his hands. 'I can't make head nor tail of it myself – but here's the story briefly. See what you can make of it.' His swift glance included them all before it moved to follow Clark. He had stopped to talk to a young couple who had just entered the room. 'He was engaged to this fabulously beautiful girl – not my type, mind,' he went on irrelevantly. 'Too shallow in my opinion; too aware of her beauty. However, every man to his own choice.

Clark fell heavily, and as he's comfortably off this girl favoured him above all the other hopefuls who hovered around like bees over a honey-pot. They got engaged and Clark was right on top of the world, but then the girl got restless and decided she wanted to go travelling. Clark just couldn't, at the time, his works manager having been disabled, and Clark's having to look to the business himself. He's in hardware in a fairly big way,' he explained. 'Wholesale. Well, to cut a long story short,' added George all of a rush as, out of the corner of his eye, he saw his friend approaching, glass in hand, 'the girl just disappeared.'

'But—' began Linda, when she was interrupted.

'She lived in a flat – had a fairly good post, too – with a newspaper. When Clark called one evening to take her out as usual he found the curtains all drawn and the flat locked up. The people next door told him she had said she'd be away a long time. She'd make arrangements for her letters to be re-directed, but these neighbours of hers hadn't been given the girl's new address.'

'You met her?' Linda looked curiously at him, speaking quickly in order to receive an answer before Clark reached the table.

'Of course I met her. Haven't I said how beautiful she is? She fairly took the place by storm, did—' He broke off, producing a smile as his friend drew near. 'You got your drink, I see. But you'll soon be ready for another.' George glanced round. 'What are you all having?' They told him and he ordered. Jill's eyes were on Clark; she noticed his brooding expression, the melancholy way in which he drooped his shoulders. He seemed enclosed within himself, and although Jill secretly believed he was better without such a girl she couldn't help feeling sorry for him.

George was plainly endeavouring to cheer him up, but without success. Clark answered his questions in monosyllables and sometimes he proffered no answer at all. But George's patience never waned; he was a most sympathetic and understanding friend to have, thought Jill, and she had an opportunity of telling him this when, on her remarking on the beautiful flower arrangements, he said impulsively,

'Come over and take a look at those in the ballroom. They've been done ready for a big wedding in the morning. You don't mind if I take Miss Sharman off for a few minutes?' he added, glancing around at the others.

'Take her by all means,' said Mrs. Mason. 'But I daresay you'll not show her anything half as exotic as the flowers she's now used to over there.'

'I think you're wonderful with Clark, no matter what you say,' Jill insisted when, having told George that he was sympathetic and understanding with Clark, her words had been swept away with a wave of George's hand. 'Anyone else would lose patience with him.'

'I'm so darned sorry for him. Just imagine a girl's leading him on as far as to become engaged to him and then to do a disappearing act. It was enough to drive him out of his mind, poor devil. I'm beginning to wonder if he'll ever get over the glamorous Sylvia de Courcy. It's a great pity they ever met—' He stopped. 'Is something wrong?'

'Sylvia de Courcy?' gasped Jill disbelievingly. 'Is that what you said?' A stupid question, she suddenly realized, so it was no wonder he stared at her with a sort of mild astonishment.

'Do you know her?'

'A girl of that name has come to stay with some neighbours of ours. This girl's very beautiful – about twenty-six or seven. Fair with lovely blue eyes . . .' She tailed off, realizing that the most amazing coincidence had occurred. 'It's the same girl, isn't it?'

George was even more staggered than Jill. He shook his head, as if trying to clear it of some intoxicating influence.

'It can't be true,' he said when at length he could speak. 'Why should she go there?'

'She came with her uncle.' Jill hesitated, staring for a moment at the great bank of flowers by which she and George stood. She was undecided about talking too much to George, but after some consideration she continued, 'It's a most odd circumstance – but she's let it be known that it's she who has been jilted.'

His eyes opened very wide.

'She – jilted? Why the devil should she say that?'

Jill shook her head, still rather dazed by what she had learned.

'It's a mystery, isn't it?'

'I don't think Clark knows she even has an uncle. I'm sure he told me she was alone in the world.'

'Well, it's her uncle she's with at present. It seems that he was a friend of the Drakes – they're the neighbours I've mentioned – and he brought Sylvia over for a long holiday, so that she could get over her broken heart.'

'Her *what* !' blazed George, having become more and more angry as he listened to what Jill had to reveal. 'I've never heard of anything so infamous!' He paused, his brow creased in thought. 'Why should she carry on like that? Have you any ideas?'

'Not one. It doesn't make sense at all.'

'It's a whole lot of nonsense!' He paused again. 'There must be some reason somewhere. The girl never struck me as having something missing upstairs.' He looked at Jill – or rather, he glared at her, just as if she were to blame for everything. 'You've no ideas, you say?'

'It's a complete mystery.'

'You've already said that.'

'Do you think . . .?' began Jill as an idea did at last emerge from the dazed state of her mind. 'You said she wanted to travel?'

'She was crazy to do so—' He stopped, eyes staring as Jill's idea was transferred to him. 'You think she might have staged the whole thing in order to excite her uncle's pity, so that he would take her away, in order to help her to forget?'

'It's too absurd for words,' protested Jill, shaking her head.

'Many aspects of this business are too absurd for words.'

'I can't imagine her leaving anyone like Clark. After all, she must have loved him, or otherwise she'd never have become engaged to him.'

'I believe – now I've heard this about her being in Africa – that she had the idea that Clark would be good for a few cushy travel tickets—' He broke off, eyes blazing. 'I don't believe she was ever in love with him, or intending to marry him.' George talked on, and by the time he had finished Jill was coming to accept the fact that Sylvia had in fact believed she would get Clark to take her travelling. When her plan was not materializing she hit on the idea of concocting a tale which would so affect her doting uncle that he would take her away in order to forget her broken romance.

'If it's true it's a wicked thing to do,' she murmured, absently fingering a soft white lily petal. The great bank of flowers spread all along one side of a raised dais, continued with greatly-reduced height across the front, then rose again at the other side. 'I'm beginning to believe that she really did act in that dreadful way, but to have done so she must be absolutely heartless.' Jill's thoughts were naturally on Dean's apparent attraction to the girl, and on the depressing possibility of his falling in love with her.

'Heartless? She's a disgrace to womanhood! Clark's as upright a chap as any girl could want – oh, I know that at the present time he must appear morose and sulky to you, but he isn't like that normally. You should have seen . . .' George tailed off, turning swiftly and glancing round. Flowers were massed behind him, and tall palms and conifers in ornate earthenware pots. 'Did you see anything?' he inquired sharply.

Jill shook her head, faintly bewildered.

'No. What—?'

'Nor hear anything?'

'I don't know what you mean?'

'I thought I heard someone – behind those flowers, and I'm sure I saw a movement. You had your back towards those particular flowers, though.'

'I expect other people are looking at the flowers,' she

pointed out reasonably, and he nodded his head.

'As I was saying, you should have seen Clark when he was telling me of his engagement. He was the happiest man in the world – no doubt about it at all.'

'It's most upsetting for him, but in my opinion he's far better off without her. If she could use him like that then she's not worth bothering about.'

'But he doesn't know she's used him. You're forgetting that point. And I can't tell him, that's for sure, much as I'd like to.'

'Of course you can't. You're not sure your conclusion's correct, anyway.'

George looked at her.

'What other explanation is there for her going about telling people she's been jilted? No, Jill, I've hit on the correct explanation – or perhaps I should say we have, because it really was your idea, even though you hadn't actually voiced it.'

'It's all very sad.' She became lost in contemplation. For such a girl to be Dean's wife ... it didn't bear thinking of, and yet it could come about, for how was Dean ever to learn what Sylvia had done? Everyone believed her to be the victim of a man who had heartlessly thrown her over; the men especially felt sympathetic towards her – even Patrick, who invariably passed lightly over everything. Was it pity which had led Dean to take Sylvia under his wing, to take her about and have her dine with him at Nyala Mount? It could be, but there was a great deal of truth in the saying that pity was akin to love.

CHAPTER SEVEN

LINDA was overwhelmed when Jill presented her with
the fan, protesting at first that it was far too valuable to
give away.

'Please have it,' begged Jill. 'You love it, and I do
want to give you something for all the help you've given
me. And another thing, your mother really must let me
pay her for my keep—'

'Don't you dare mention anything like that to her,'
interrupted Linda rather hotly. 'You should know my
mum by now. She'd go hairless!'

Jill had to laugh.

'Then suggest a present for her too,' she requested,
spreading a hand in an inviting gesture. In the room
chosen for putting aside what Jill intended to keep
there were treasures of all kinds, from exquisite Chelsea
and Meissen, to ivory and jade figures and beautiful
Georgian silver. There was furniture too – Chippendale
and Sheraton, and there were two beautiful china cabi-
nets which Jill could not bear to leave even though she
wondered where they would go when she at last got
them to Bangali Farm.

'She really doesn't want anything,' began Linda, but
Jill was already picking up a silver cruet.

'She likes anything dainty like this. No matter what
you say,' she added as her friend began shaking her
head. 'I'm giving it to her.'

'Very well . . .' Linda was flicking open the fan. 'I

never imagined I'd ever own anything so exquisite,' she murmured, wafting the fan close to her face. 'I shall have a really beautiful frame made for it – I know just the man for the job; he renovates antiques with what can only be described as loving care. He'll be in his element putting this into a frame. He uses old wood, of course. He buys old furniture and if he can't make anything of a renovation then he keeps the wood to use on something else.'

Jill smiled happily at her friend's expression, herself deriving immense pleasure from the gift she had made.

'I suppose we had better be getting on,' she said when at length Linda put down the fan on the table, beside the cruet which Jill had put to one side. 'There's no end to this stuff. I'd no idea there was so much – but of course I'd only been in one of the upstairs rooms, that in which Mrs. Pointon slept.'

'It's a pity you can't keep the lot,' said Linda regretfully. 'I know we've sorted out the best, but we've had to be exceptionally selective. For instance, if it were me I should be wanting to keep that lovely secretaire; the design and inlay are so exquisite.'

'I know,' sighed Jill, biting her lip. 'It was a hard decision to make, but I've got to draw the line somewhere. Our house is not large, and in any case I can't clutter up a place that isn't mine, can I?'

'No, I suppose not.'

Jill hesitated.

'You know, Linda,' she said at length, 'I think I'll put most of these things in store. Why should I sell them when I've no need?'

'That's a splendid idea! Why didn't we think of it before? It'll be there when you get married and have a home of your own.'

Jill gave a deprecating shrug.

'I can't see myself married . . .' And she tailed off in so dismal a manner that Linda gave her a sharp glance of interrogation.

'You're not in love with someone unattainable, are you?'

Jill gave a start.

'Whatever made you ask a question like that?'

'The way you spoke.' Linda's eyes became perceptive. 'You are, aren't you?'

A long pause and then,

'Yes, as a matter of fact, I am.' And as Linda was obviously expecting her to continue Jill told her about Dean, and the bad beginning they had made, owing to her own initial dislike of him.

'I wouldn't give up hope, if I were you,' was Linda's response when at length Jill had stopped speaking. 'He brought you to the airport, which seems to suggest he was more than a little concerned about you.'

'He did it mainly because of Bob's inability to do so.' Jill explained about the snake bite and how it had resulted in Bob's having to stay at home with Lucie. 'You see, Bob was intending to come to England with me,' she ended, and as Linda made no further comment Jill said again that they had better get on with their work.

'We'll have to go through everything once more, now you've decided to put most of the stuff in store,' pointed out Linda, and Jill nodded in agreement.

'I have another four days before my return flight.

That should be long enough to see to everything, don't you think?'

'Yes; leave the listing to me.' Linda glanced around. 'You're having everything in this room shipped to Africa, is that right?'

'Yes.'

'And most of the other put into store—?' Linda broke off, jerking her head. 'The doorbell. Must be a pedlar; I'll go.'

'Clark!' The startled exclamation came clearly to Jill as she stood by the table, gazing down at the fan. 'What are you doing here?'

'I want to speak to Miss Sharman.'

'You do?' Linda sounded nonplussed, as well she might. Jill went into the hall and stared at Clark for a long moment before saying,

'You want me? What for?'

He glanced at Linda and said it was a private matter. The two girls exchanged glances. Jill said,

'You can speak before Linda. Er – you'd better step inside,' she added, remembering her manners. 'We're untidy . . .' She tailed off. Why should she have to explain away the state of the house to a stranger?

'I'll go upstairs and begin making out that list I mentioned,' said Linda, and disappeared.

Clark breathed an audible sigh of relief.

'I didn't really want to speak in front of anyone else—' He looked at Jill with a pleading expression in his honest grey eyes. 'I overheard you and George talking – when we were at the Abbey Royal. I came into the ballroom; I was restless and wandering about, and I somehow got mixed up with the flowers at the back of where you two were standing. It was obvious from the conversation that George had told you about my fiancée's disappearance, so I won't go into that. What I came to see you about was—' He broke off as Linda appeared at the top of the stairs.

'Sorry to interrupt, Jill,' she called, 'but must I list all of the furniture in the side bedroom?'

'All except the bed. It's an old-fashioned heavy thing and it doesn't match the suite.'

'Okay.' Linda disappeared and Clark began speaking again. Jill listened, gathering that Clark had learned where Jill was from something that was said during the conversation at the hotel.

'You can't come back with me,' Jill told him firmly when, after telling her that he still loved Sylvia and must get in touch with her again, he had asked if he could accompany Jill when she left for her home in Africa. 'It's not my affair and I don't want anything to do with it.'

'I'm not asking you to have anything to do with it. I only want to go back with you, so that I can get in touch with Sylvia.'

Jill shook her head, pointing out that if Sylvia wanted to marry him she would never have gone off like that.

'I'm only sorry you listened,' she added. 'Your knowledge has come accidentally and I think you should forget it.'

'Forget it? How can I, when I've been trying frantically to find her? My happening to overhear you and George was providential – it was meant to be. I *must* get to her, Miss Sharman,' he said with a break in his voice. 'I can't live without her!'

Jill bit her lip. Little did she know when talking to George what the outcome of her revelation would be. Only now, when it was too late, did she regret mentioning Sylvia – but at the time she had been so taken by surprise at George's mentioning of the girl's name that she had spoken impulsively, quite without thinking.

'I can't prevent you from going to South Africa,' she admitted. 'But I can't let you come with me. It would look as if I were interfering.' Naturally her thoughts flitted to Dean, and to the probable result should Clark suddenly turn up and let it be known that he hadn't jilted Sylvia at all. Dean would be just about as disgusted as he could be – or would he? Perhaps even by now his feelings for the girl were such that he could overlook her perfidy, and even be glad that her engagement was in fact broken.

'No such thing,' began Clark, when she interrupted him.

'You're no longer engaged to Sylvia, and were I in your position I'd try to forget her.'

'No longer engaged? Certainly I'm engaged! I haven't thrown her over!'

'But she's thrown you over.' Jill knew this was cruel, but she failed to find any kinder way in which to bring home to him the stark truth, that Sylvia no longer cared for him.

'No, she hasn't. She just went away – for a holiday,' declared Clark with a stubborn edge to his voice. 'She'll come round once she sees me – Oh, I can guess what you're thinking, but I happen to know her – very well. She loves me. This bug got into her and she was determined to travel. I've thought over what you and George

125

were saying about her ruse to get her uncle to take her away. I did know about this uncle, by the way, and she had mentioned that he doted on her. I never bothered to learn from her just where he lived, so I couldn't get in touch with him when she disappeared.' He paused, but Jill could find nothing to say and he continued, 'As I said, I thought about the conclusions you and George had reached, and agreed that Sylvia had deliberately lied so that her uncle would take her away. But I'll stake all I own on being able to get her back.'

Jill sighed, pity still strong within her as, dwelling on the situation and putting herself in the place of an en-gaged girl – a girl in love – she could not for the life of her understand Sylvia's action. For Jill love would mean the desire always to be near the loved one. Certainly never could she by one small act bring hurt to the man she loved and had promised to marry.

'I'm determined to see her,' Clark was saying in a strong determined tone. 'If you won't agree to my coming with you then at least you'll tell me where she's staying?'

'I don't know . . .' replied Jill undecidedly. At the back of her mind there quite naturally lurked the hope that nothing would come of the affair between Sylvia and Dean, and if by some miracle Clark could manage to reawaken some spark in Sylvia, then undoubtedly Jill's own position might be improved. After all, Dean had liked her once – liked her enough to mention a desire to get to know her better. The more Jill pondered the whole situation the more she realized just how little different she was from any other girl in love. She wanted Dean – no use denying this. And here presented to her was a chance of bringing back into Sylvia's life the man to whom she had been engaged . . . The temptation was too great, especially with Clark's confidence that he could win Sylvia back.

'Thank you, Miss Sharman,' Clark said gratefully when she gave him the address of the Drakes. 'Thank you very much indeed.' He was writing it down and a moment later the little pocket notebook was put safely away. 'I'm terribly grateful to you.' A smile lit his face; Jill was reminded of what George had said about Clark's not being a naturally morose person. He seemed quite happy now, obviously supremely optimistic about the coming meeting with the girl whom he maintained was still his fiancée. 'We'll probably be meeting again – a long way from here!' His optimism increasing to jubilation within a matter of seconds, he was turning to go, his step light and springy as he passed through the front door. 'Incidentally, I haven't mentioned anything to George about my intention of getting into contact with you?' The statement was also a request and Jill answered quietly,

'I don't suppose I shall be seeing George again.'

'No.' He paused. 'Maybe I shall have to tell him of my plans. He'll consider me quite mad, though, because like you he feels I'd be better off without Sylvia.'

Jill made no comment on this and as Clark reached the gate she closed the door, turning with a sigh of resignation as Linda came down the stairs, an inquiring expression on her face.

Dean was there waiting when the plane touched down. His appearance brought an instant smile to her face and his eyes flickered, faintly mocking, but there was also present a noticeable element of pleasure.

'It would appear that you're glad to see me,' he observed, and she flushed daintily as she said yes, she was. But of course she went on immediately to ask why Bob hadn't been able to meet her and was told to her relief that it had nothing to do with Lucie, who was now fully recovered, but that as Dean had business to do which brought him reasonably close to the airport he had naturally offered to pick her up. Jill glanced suspiciously at him, saw an expressionless mask and so was unable to deduce whether or not this was strictly the truth. All she did know was that a warmth filled her whole body at the knowledge that Dean had taken the trouble to be here, awaiting her arrival.

'How did you get on?' he was inquiring once they were on their way. 'Did you get some help, as I advised?'

'Yes; my friend helped. As it happened she was on holiday, and she spent the whole of it helping me.'

'I'm glad. I suppose you've arranged for most of the things to be disposed of, and also the house?'

'The house, yes. But there was so much really beautiful stuff that in the end I decided to put most of it in store. Some special pieces I'm having brought here, and a few things I didn't care for I've left to be sold.'

'You've stored most, you say?'

'Yes. A big London firm will be taking it.'

'It'll cost you a lot of money, surely?'

'It is rather expensive,' she admitted. 'But somehow I was loath to part with it. I shall never again have the opportunity of getting so much beautiful furniture, for instance. Antiques are becoming so rare that people tend to hold on to them.'

Dean nodded in agreement.

'I think you've been wise,' he mused. 'The appreciation will far exceed the cost of storage.' They were passing through the lovely suburb a mile or two from the airport and Jill gave a small sigh of contentment at once again being confronted by familiar trees and flowers, and even the white sultry heat was welcome. She gazed from her side window at the soft peaceful scene of gardens spilling over with exotic flowers and tall swaying palm trees and, her imagination ignited, she could smell the perfumes, even see golden moths hovering on the still tropical air, or settling on the flowers, seeking for nectar.

'I never, never want to leave again,' she murmured, quite unaware she had spoken her thoughts audibly until her companion, twisting swiftly to slant her a glance, said, an odd expression in his voice,

'Your visit to England didn't create any nostalgia, then?'

'It was pleasant to see the old places, and the friends with whom I stayed, but I'm glad to be back.' Her voice as low and sweet, and deeply sincere. 'It's very true that Africa calls as no other continent ever can.'

Dean looked ahead, to the long white road, tree-lined, with a thick hedge of scarlet bougainvillaea running down the centre, separating the two carriageways.

'You're settled for life, then?'

'I – I expect so.' Her faltering voice brought his head round again.

'You're not quite sure?'

There was the merest hesitation as Jill allowed a fleeting vision to intrude – the vision of Dean and Sylvia as man and wife. But she cast it away; this lovely drive, with Dean beside her, was not for spoiling with so dismal a picture.

'Yes, Dean, I am sure. I could never be perfectly happy anywhere else – not now.'

They drove in silence for a long while before Dean slowed down by a small roadside café where the tables were set in a terraced garden with shady casuarina trees and palms dotted about, lending protection from the fierce sun while at the same time allowing slanting rays to pierce their bright green foliage, and fall on to the lawn.

'I expect you're ready for a little refreshment?' Dean was already turning into the gravelly path, taking her agreement for granted. The tyres crunched and sent gravel spinning to hit the trunks of the eucalyptus trees growing on both sides of the narrow driveway.

A white-coated native boy waited on the table, fetching them tea and cakes and a pineapple sundae with cream.

'That was lovely!' exclaimed Jill when they had finished. 'I didn't realize just how ready for it I was.'

Dean looked at her; she became rather painfully conscious of her unruly hair and automatically glanced up at his, saw a few strands being teased by the breeze and felt a little better.

'Tell me about your friends?' he said unexpectedly. 'Did they take you out at all?'

'We had a meal out on my last evening; and on another evening we went to a very plush country hotel for drinks.' She refrained from mentioning Clark, naturally. Dean would soon know of his existence, though, as he would be arriving quite soon.

Dean smiled, a rather indulgent smile that sent a delicious little tingle rippling through her veins.

'You've been living it up by the sound of things,' he teased. 'I wish I'd been there.'

'You do?' Jill made an effort to control her rising emotions, but her voice was more than a little shaky as she added, 'I wish you had, too.'

His intent gaze was piercing yet unfathomable.

'In that case,' he decided presently, 'you and I will go somewhere "very plush" and live it up.'

'Oh . . . sh-shall we?'

'I take it you're not averse to the idea?'

What exactly was he trying to convey to her? She sensed there was something important underlying his invitation, and she found it thrilling because of its very obscurity.

'On the contrary,' she replied, determinedly taking herself in hand, 'I'm greatly enamoured with it.'

Dean laughed, his eyes reflecting his amusement as they met hers across the table.

'We appear to be progressing,' he commented, but entered into no further explanation, so that once again Jill was pleasantly affected by his vagueness.

Ten minutes later they were driving away from the café, and later still when the main highway was left behind they came to real country, with fields of maize and soya beans, and wattle plantations in the distance. A winding river bed could be picked out by the high eucalyptus trees flourishing along its banks, their foliage unmoving, as a stillness had now fallen over the shimmering, heat-hazed bushveld.

Jill put up a hand to stifle a yawn and Dean turned half-smilingly towards her.

'Tired?' he inquired indulgently. 'Shall I stop and let you get in the back? You can then stretch yourself out.'

She shook her head.

'I'm not all that tired,' she assured him.

'I thought you were; you'd become so quiet.'

'I was only thinking.'

'About what?'

She gave a small shrug.

'Nothing in particular.' A pause, and then, 'I'm beginning to feel horribly selfish and guilty about what I've decided to have shipped over here. After all, it is Lucie's house, and I haven't even asked her if I can bring the things to Bangali Farm.'

'I shouldn't think she'll mind. Is there a lot?'

'A fair amount.'

'If there's anything you want to store I can take it for you. I've a couple of rooms that are never used. Take advantage of my offer if you feel you've too much for comfort.'

'Thank you, Dean. You're very kind.'

He smiled faintly at this and she sensed that for a fleeting moment some sardonic comment hovered on his lips. But whatever he had meant to say was stemmed and he fell silent for a while, remarking much later that it was going to thunder. Jill glanced up at the sky and agreed. The atmosphere had become oppressive, the air stiller than ever with not even a leaf stirring. Over on the edge of a maize field two scantily-clad natives astride donkeys glanced upwards and spoke together, one of them pointing away towards the higher land to the east. Warm moist air was rising rapidly, causing a state of extreme instability. The sun was going down and above the hills the convection currents were building up to create a huge cumulonimbus cloud from which must inevitably result thunder, lightning and heavy rain.

'There it is,' said Jill unnecessarily as the first low rumble echoed through the silence.

'I expect we shall be forced to stop again,' predicted Dean, but went on to say that time did not matter on this occasion.

Lightning soon followed the thunder, and finally came the rain, which quickly reached torrential proportions. Pulling in to the side of the road, Dean stopped the car and switched off the engine.

Time passed and still the deluge persisted. Glancing at Dean, Jill saw the pursed lips, the fixed stare at the road ahead, practically invisible in the rain and mist. Darkness was falling rapidly, and the lightning became more vivid in consequence. It was a strange world of semi-darkness, with breaks caused by the lightning and the low growls of thunder at last dying away into the distance. Hailstones fell, having been enlarged to enormous sizes by being carried upwards over and over again by the strong vertical currents, and collecting layer upon layer of super-cooled water in the process, until, in the end, their weight could no longer be supported by the updraught.

'What a violent thing a thunderstorm is,' Jill murmured when at long last the downpour gave way to light rain.

'A great many aspects of nature are violent,' he commented, starting up the car again and easing it on to the road.

'Surely there will be floods after this?'

'I'm just hoping we don't come upon any we can't negotiate.' But they had gone only a couple of miles when they reached a stretch of the road which was completely under water. 'I wonder . . .?'

'It might be too deep,' she warned nervously. 'It looks almost like a lake.'

'It certainly seems to stretch a long way. The road's low here, for about half a mile, although I shouldn't think it'll all be under water.' He paused and Jill knew he was considering taking a chance and driving through it. But he shook his head at length and gave a sigh of resignation. 'We'd better go back and take the other road.' He glanced at her. 'I'm sorry, Jill, but I'm not going to get you home much before midnight.'

'It doesn't matter. Perhaps we can phone Bob a little later?'

'There's an hotel on the other road—' He glanced at his petrol gauge. 'I think we can just about make it. There's a petrol station there as well.'

Jill awoke and glanced around, memory flooding in as she noted the unfamiliar furnishings and drapes. She and Dean had been compelled to stay the night at the hotel, which they had just managed to reach before running out of petrol. The road was flooded about a mile farther on, the proprietor had told Dean, so he and Jill had no choice other than to leave the completion of their journey until the morning, when it was expected the waters would have subsided.

Glancing from the window when she had got out of bed, Jill watched the screen of dawn widen as flaring crimson rays intruded into the opal shades enveloping the drowsy bushveld. Tall palms growing in the hotel garden were etched against the lurid glare; this was the wonder of Africa with all its natural phenomena. Jill let the lovely picture fade from view as she brought her attention a little closer, to the garden itself where gay canna flowers and bougainvillaeas and other tropical treasures claimed her interest before, turning, she went over to the basin and washed her face and hands, the thought of taking breakfast with Dean bringing a happy smile to hover on her lips when presently she was before the mirror brushing her hair.

The flow of her thoughts stopped, then became retrospective on the instant and she was having dinner in a low-ceilinged, dimly-lit room overlooking the illuminated hotel gardens; the windows were wide open, letting in the 'after-rain' smell of newly-watered vegetation, and the night-sounds of insects and the pulse of a native drum-beat from a distant kraal.

It had been an intimate, friendly meal, with a chat afterwards over coffee. Dean had later left Jill outside her bedroom door, and his expression as he said good night set her heart beating wildly ... and her hopes soaring in harmony with it.

CHAPTER EIGHT

LUCIE and Bob were on the stoep when Dean drove up to Bangali Farm a little after eleven o'clock.

'You've been having an adventure, by the sound of things.' Bob looked from Jill to Dean and a curious expression entered his eyes. 'It was lucky you made the hotel before your petrol ran out.'

Dean grimaced and nodded.

'I see you've felt the brunt too—' His keen eyes took in the many small gullies where water had run down towards the river, taking precious top-soil with it.

'The place was like a small sea. However, it's one of those things one has to get used to.' Bob shrugged resignedly and said something about the advantages of timber-growing as compared to general farming. Jill was talking to Lucie, expressing her delight at seeing her look in the pink of health after her ordeal with the snake.

'Tell me all about what you've been doing,' urged Lucie. 'You said on the phone last night that you're having a lot of stuff brought over here?'

'If you don't mind, Lucie? I feel rather guilty, because it'll not go into my room, even stacked up.'

'We'll find somewhere for it to go.'

'Dean's kindly offered to store some for me if we can't find room for all of it.'

'He has?' with a swift side glance in his direction. 'That's very kind of him.' There was a distinctly subtle note in Lucie's tone and Jill found herself colouring. 'You appear to have resolved your differences.' Lucie observed in a low tone.

'Yes, I think we have,' returned Jill happily. 'Dean's been wonderful.'

'Wonderful?' with an amused inflection.

Jill gave a small unsteady laugh.

'He never complained, or even showed any signs of impatience even, at the inconvenience he'd been caused through coming to meet me at the airport.'

'He most probably enjoyed all the delays and the stay at the hotel . . . as, it would appear, you yourself did.'

The colour in Jill's cheeks deepened.

'It was rather pleasant,' she admitted, and automatically her eyes flitted towards Dean, standing with one foot on the lower step of the stoep, and one hand half tucked into the pocket of his jacket. He saw her glance and a smile touched the corners of his mouth.

'I must be off,' he decided, returning his attention to Bob. 'I shall be over tomorrow, probably, to fetch those young trees – the oranges and naartjes I promised you. They're in fibre pots, so they'll take all right, especially now that we've had such heavy rain.'

The three watched the car crunch away, to disappear eventually as a bend was taken.

'Come on in and I'll make you some coffee.' Lucie tucked an arm through Jill's. 'We want to hear all about it. It sounds as if you've got some beautiful things?'

'I have, Lucie – just wait until you see them!'

'You never knew the old lady had so much?'

'No; she had stacks of stuff in the loft, and the bed-rooms were crammed as well. She did tell me once that she and her husband lived in a much larger house when they were first married.' Jill talked on while they drank their coffee. 'I'm told that it will be several weeks before the things arrive,' she ended.

'You did all that was necessary, though, about the shipping of them?'

'I left it to the solicitors to do that. They're selling the house, too, and also the few items I decided I didn't want.'

Jill made no mention of meeting Clark, mainly because she was now in doubt about his coming out to look up the girl who had played him so mean a trick. On giving the matter more consideration he would undoubtedly change his mind, thought Jill.

But it was to transpire that she was wrong, for he arrived two days later and telephoned her from an hotel in Breysburg, where he was putting up. He had managed to obtain her telephone number from one of the shopkeepers in town, after inquiring around for a while.

'But why have you got in touch with me?' asked Jill, puzzled.

'Because it's suddenly dawned on me that I can't go, quite openly, and visit Sylvia at the address you've given me.'

'Why not?'

'She's spread it around that she's been jilted, and in addition to having induced her uncle to take pity on her she's also basking in the sympathy of everyone around here. Were I to denounce her she'd be finished with me for ever.'

'Why didn't you think of this before now?' Jill

couldn't help asking impatiently.

'I really don't know,' he admitted. 'On discovering where she was I suppose I acted precipitately, believing I had only to appear on the scene and she'd have me back immediately. I never stopped to think about snags.'

'What, then, do you intend doing?'

'I shall have to move cautiously. I wondered if you would help me?'

'In what way?' inquired Jill guardedly.

'I can explain if you'll meet me—?'

'I don't think I want to be involved,' she interrupted at once, thinking more of her new relationship with Dean than anything else. To be seen with another man was something she instinctively wished to avoid.

'But, please, Miss Sharman. I'm not intending to ask the impossible.' He sounded flat and disconsolate and she found herself touched by sympathy. 'I must talk to someone, and I thought I might take you out to dinner?'

She hesitated, and while she did he began pleading more strongly. At last she agreed to meet him and have a meal, but not at the Springbok Club which he instantly mentioned. Dean could just be there, she thought, and she was taking no risks.

She had to give some sort of explanation to Bob and Lucie, and as this could scarcely be done without revealing Clark's engagement to Sylvia Jill was forced to relate the whole extraordinary story to her astonished listeners, ending by stressing that the secret must be kept.

'But what a rotten trick!' denounced Bob. 'The man

must be crazy to want the girl back.'

'It's love, Bob,' smiled Lucie. 'It does strange things to people.'

He gave her a frowning look.

'It certainly wouldn't do anything as strange as that to me,' he declared emphatically, and Lucie gave a grimace as she glanced at her sister-in-law.

'So you're dining with him this evening?' she said, changing the trend of conversation.

'Yes, that's right.' Jill glanced at her brother. 'Is it all right if I take the car?'

'Of course.'

Having bought a new dress in England Jill decided to wear it. Of a pretty shade of coral, it had long full sleeves gathered into wide cuffs, and a narrow roll collar which came high up her throat. She felt good in it and wished it were Dean with whom she was going out to dine.

Clark was waiting as she drove up to the front of the Mayfair Hotel. He smiled and told her she looked nice, a compliment which meant nothing, she decided, being made in so absent-minded a fashion. Plainly his mind was occupied by something far more important than his companion's attire.

'You booked a table?' She managed a smile, but she had very little enthusiasm for the evening ahead.

'Yes. But it was unnecessary as there's hardly a soul in there from what I can see.' He indicated the window as he spoke and Jill glanced across as she locked the door of the car. From within the room a rosy light glowed. giving it an intimate aspect but also revealing that what Clark had said was true. Jill could see only three couples seated at tables widely separated from one another.

The waiter appeared as they entered, and they were conducted to a table in a corner, well away from everyone else. When the meal was ordered Clark said, right out of the blue,

'Do you know anything about a man called Dean Lester?'

'Dean?' She glanced swiftly at him. 'Why do you ask?'

Clark's mouth tightened.

'I've heard his name coupled with that of Sylvia—'

'You have?' The beautiful Sylvia had become unimportant during that happy interlude she had recently spent with Dean. 'Already?'

'So you knew about it?' Clark's eyes glinted. 'Why didn't you warn me?' he asked accusingly.

Her face had paled a little. She said rather stiffly,

'What reason was there for my mentioning it? I don't expect there's anything serious in the friendship.' Was the wish father to the thought? she wondered, dejection creeping over her.

'I wouldn't know whether there's anything serious in the affair—' He stopped and a frown gathered on his forehead. 'After I phoned you I wandered around the town for a while and then went into the Grand for a drink. I got talking to two blokes and casually asked if there were any beautiful unattached girls about. I was too late, one of them said, grinning at the other. There had been a new arrival – a Sylvia de Courcy – who was certainly beautiful, but who had very soon been snapped up by an eligible bachelor by the name of Dean Lester. He grows trees!' The last sentence came out on an explosive, disparaging note, just as if there was something ignominious about timber-growing. 'They've been going about together, especially during this past ten days.'

This past ten days ... The last of Jill's buoyancy dissolved; she would never have believed she could be reduced from happiness to black despair in so short a time. Clark was speaking again, asking what she knew about Dean Lester.

'He's a neighbour of ours,' she informed him, wishing with all her heart that she had not agreed to come out with Clark. Still, she supposed it were better that she know that Dean and Sylvia had been going about together for the whole time that she, Jill, had been away in England.

'What's he like? Attractive?'

'Very.' She was thinking of that journey, and the intimacy that had sprung up between Dean and herself.

'You think she might fall for him?'

'You've said she's in love with you,' Jill reminded him stiffly.

'I was optimistic until I heard about this other bloke. Is he well off?'

'I expect he is,' Jill replied non-committally, feeling this aspect was irrelevant since Clark himself was also comfortably off.

'She spread it around that she's been jilted—' Clark shook his head as if he still couldn't quite believe this. 'Men feel sorry for girls who've been so shabbily treated.' He threw Jill a glance. 'It could be pity he feels for her?'

She nodded her head.

'It could be. Everyone felt sorry for her.'

Clark's mouth compressed.

'How could she lie like that?' he said indignantly. 'Imagine a girl thinking up such a ruse just to gain her uncle's pity so that he'd take her travelling. Had I thought for one moment that she'd go to these lengths I'd have managed somehow to take time off and have given her a trip abroad myself. We could have got married for that matter and taken a trip abroad for our honeymoon.'

The first course was put before them and they began to eat in silence. But after a while Clark brought up the matter of the help he had previously mentioned.

'As I can't present myself as Sylvia's fiancé I must have some sort of excuse for being here, and I wondered if you'd tell everyone that you and I met in England and that you invited me over for a holiday—' He stopped as she shook her head.

'I'm sorry, Clark, but I'm not becoming involved in this business.'

'You can't deny we met in England.' A sharp edge to his voice now and a glint of anger in his eye.

'True, but I am not going to let it be known that I invited you over for a holiday.'

'Have you some reason for this refusal?'

She stared at him with resentment on hearing this question. He was still almost a stranger to her and as such he had no right to be putting questions to her.

'As a matter of fact I have,' she said at last.

'But I can't imagine what that reason could be?'

'It's a private reason.'

'I seem to have upset you,' he observed.

Jill gave an impatient sigh.

'Shall we let the matter drop?' she asked, but to her surprise he was totally unperturbed by her abruptly-spoken question.

'I'd like to know the reason, because I might as well tell you that I'm going to let it be known that you and I met in England. I haven't any other excuse for being here.' He paused, evidently expecting her to relent and give him the reason, but she remained obstinately silent.

'Sylvia's my life, and I intend to fight to get her back. This isn't the sort of place one chooses for a holiday, and so, as I've said, I must have an excuse for being here. It's so simple for you to help me in this; all you have to do is go about with me a little, just so that people will accept my story that you invited me over here. Of course I must get in touch with Sylvia first.'

'I'm not going about with you, Mr. —'

'Call me Clark – please. Can I call you Jill?'

'If you wish,' she replied coldly.

'Won't you help me?' His tones were coaxing now, but Jill retained an inexorable expression. 'It isn't asking much . . .' His voice began to trail away and Jill glanced up. 'This fellow's coming over here,' said Clark, puzzled.

Tingles ran along Jill's spine even before she twisted her head. Dean was already close to the table; a couple of steps brought him to it.

'Jill . . . you're—' He stopped, then began again, explaining that he had seen Bob's car as he was passing and naturally expected to find the three of them dining together. His eyes had settled on her face after flickering over Clark's; she flushed under the intense and questioning regard. Having made the introductions she watched the look of animosity spring into Clark's eyes as he shook hands with Dean. And then Clark spoke, before she could do so, and she just sat and gaped as, having told Dean that he and Jill had met when she was in England, he went on to say, avoiding Jill's eyes,

'She invited me over for a holiday. Her descriptions of the country were so attractive that I decided to take advantage of her invitation and come. I'm hoping she's going to take me around.'

Bereft of speech at the lie, Jill could only continue to stare at him, but he still avoided her eyes.

'I see,' from Dean in clipped and frigid tones. But there was a sort of astonishment in his gaze and . . . could it be a trace of hurt? wondered Jill, a terrible bleakness sweeping over her. She opened her mouth, then closed it again. What could she say without denouncing Clark as a liar? 'I'm sorry I intruded, Jill. Good night.'

'Dean – wait, I . . .' He was striding across the room towards the door and she turned to Clark, her cheeks flaming with anger. 'What made you tell a pack of lies like that?' she demanded. 'Dean's a – a – fr-friend of mine—' To her dismay her eyes filled with tears; she brushed a hand across them, aware of the widening of Clark's own eyes as perception dawned.

'Oh, I say, I'm sorry—'

'Sorry!' she flashed. 'It's too late to be sorry! Why did you lie, I said?'

'I thought he'd pass it all on to Sylvia – or at any rate, spread it around. I thought only of making her jealous, and had no idea I was saying anything that would hurt you.'

Too unhappy to say more, Jill found a handkerchief and rubbed her eyes hard before the tears of anger and frustration were able to fall. Fate was against her, she decided; she and Dean would never get together, so she might as well relinquish all hope.

She could see again Dean's expression just now, and the surprise that had been in his eyes at the intimate situation in which he had found her – with another man. She saw Clark's insolent eyes, taking Dean's measure, while Dean himself, so tall and superior in a lightweight tropical suit, with snow-white shirt collar gleaming against his dark throat, merely gave Clark a superficial glance before saying his brief good night.

'I want to go now,' she was saying a short while later, taking up her handbag from the back of her chair.

'What about coffee?'

She shook her head.

'I want to go,' she repeated.

'All right—'

'I'll give you a lift if you want one.' This she felt she had to offer, although the sooner she bade Clark good-bye the better she would like it.

'Thanks a lot, Jill.' He would have put a hand under her elbow as they moved down the room, but she twisted away, frowning heavily. 'I'm so sorry,' he began again, and despite the impatient shrug of her shoulders he continued, 'I didn't stop to think, but I do see now what your reason was for not wanting to help me in the way I suggested. I wish you'd told me.'

He didn't wish it as much as she did, thought Jill, but

merely said,

'My refusal to help should have been enough for you.'

'Yes, I do realize that now.' He paused uncomfortably. 'The man's appearance on the scene was such a surprise. He obviously isn't with Sylvia tonight,' he added with sudden brightness, and, so it seemed to Jill, forgetting already what he had done to her by his deliberate lie.

'Obviously.' They were stepping into the darkness and the whirr of cicadas met their ears. A young moon hung above the hills, bringing a night-light softness to the slumbering landscape, and on the breeze drifted heady whiffs of perfume from the flowers in the hotel garden. Jill found nothing attractive in the African night; her heart was too heavy for appreciation.

Dean had to call at Bangali Farm the following morning, as he had promised to give Bob some advice about planting wattles on a large tract of land which up till now had not been used for anything, as it was covered with sparse mixed bush. Lucie naturally made coffee which they drank on the stoep where the shade was cool and the breeze whipped gently round the side of the house to stir the bougainvillaea vine that grew up the wooden pillars at each end of the stoep. It was a pleasant place at all times, but especially so when the sun was high and fierce, as it was this morning, shining with brittle intensity that created a haze over the veld and the kopjes in the near distance. Dean sat down, stretching his long legs out in front of him; Lucie brought out the coffee on a tray, calling to Jill, who was in the dairy, scouring out the milk cans. She came reluctantly, her wide eyes meeting those of Dean, half afraid, half questioning. She saw an expressionless mask, heard a polite but lukewarm greeting.

'Good morning, Jill.'

'Good morning, Dean.' Her voice was low; she wondered what his reaction would be were he to know just how unhappy she felt. 'Bob's coming in a few minutes.'

'Pour the coffee, Jill,' said Lucie. 'I'm just going to butter some scones.'

'You never mentioned this boy-friend you'd met on your visit to England.' Dean spoke casually, his eyes narrowed so that she was unable to read their expression.

'He isn't a boy-friend,' she denied. 'I was introduced to him on the evening when we went to that hotel I told you about.'

'The very plush one? Yes, I remember.'

She hesitated, the urge to tell him the whole truth strong within her, but she refrained, for even though she now thoroughly disliked Clark she could not bring herself to denounce him as a liar.

'He didn't really come to see me,' she said eventually, and Dean's brows rose a fraction.

'No? But he said he did.'

'He implied that,' she corrected.

'Are we splitting hairs?' Crisp tones and faintly contemptuous. Jill moved over to the table and picked up the coffee-pot; silence reigned while she poured the steaming milky fluid into the cups. Suddenly the silence was broken as over the air, from the maize field in which

148

four of the native boys were working, there drifted their song, a sad, haunting song of Africa. 'I spoke to you, Jill,' softly from Dean as she put down the pot again. 'That fellow you were with last night said he'd come in response to an invitation from you, so obviously it's you he's come to see.'

'It's not—' She stopped, and looked rather pleadingly at him, as if, subconsciously, she was asking him to probe further on his own account, to remember the comradeship which had been theirs during that journey, and to draw from that the conclusion – which to Jill seemed so very logical – that he himself had become more important to her than any other man in the world. But his eyes glinted with that steely look she knew so well, and his mouth was tight, inflexible. If only she could be sure that he had begun to care ... She could then have made some endeavour to soften him, but she had been given no tangible sign that her own feelings were reciprocated by him. In addition there was the stark fact of his going about with Sylvia for the whole of the period while she herself was in England. Really, she thought, there was no reason at all why she should have begun to cherish the thought that he was beginning to care for her. If he was beginning to care for anyone it would seem that it was the glamorous Sylvia de Courcy. 'I just can't explain, Dean,' she said helplessly at last. 'And – and I'd rather not talk about it, if you don't mind.' She was oblivious of the fact that misery had brought a sharpness to her voice, or that the avoidance of his eyes could be misinterpreted.

'I don't mind in the least,' came the stiffly polite response, and Jill gave a little sigh of relief on seeing

Bob approaching through a small copse of flowering gum trees. Just as if some telepathic message had been conveyed to him Bob guessed at the coolness hanging between the two on the stoep. His eyes flickered from one to the other before he spoke, easing the tension.

'Good morning, Dean. It's good of you to come over like this; you must be busy on your own account?'

'The boys know what to do,' he returned casually, glancing up with a smile as Lucie appeared with the scones. For the next few minutes the conversation centred on the projected wattle plantation, with Jill silent and Lucie merely putting in a word here and there. Bob was still conscious of the tense atmosphere existing between his sister and Dean; Jill came in for one or two odd glances, but eventually, their coffee finished and the delicious hot scones eaten, the two men strolled away and were soon lost to sight. Jill rose and began piling the crockery on to the tray, while Lucie went off to resume her work in the kitchen. After washing up Jill went back to the dairy, her mind on Clark, and the dirty trick he had done on her; then her thoughts flitted to Sylvia and Dean. She wondered if Clark would succeed in winning her back, and sincerely hoped he would.

About half an hour later Dean appeared at the open door of the dairy. Jill glanced up to see him, immaculate as ever despite the fact that he had on a pair of jeans that had obviously had plenty of wear, and a short-sleeved checked shirt. She herself brushed a hand through her hair, conscious as always of the unruly pieces at the front.

'I've invited Bob and Lucie to a barbecue on Saturday evening,' he told her coolly. 'The invitation is yours too – if you care to come?'

She coloured at his manner, hesitating about her reply. She had no desire to see Dean giving all his attention to Sylvia, who would undoubtedly be there. On the other hand, she would have to give some explanation to Lucie and Bob if she refused.

'Thank you,' she said at last. 'I'd like to come.'

'It took you long enough to decide,' he returned mercilessly, and her colour deepened. 'Were you debating on whether or not you'd prefer to be with your boy-friend?'

'I've said he's not my boy-friend,' she retorted, dejection giving way to anger. 'I merely met him, as I told you, that night when we all went together to the hotel. He's practically a stranger to me.'

Dean's lips compressed.

'Be honest, Jill. Where does all this pretence get you?' She made no reply and he went on remorselessly, 'No man is going to come out to a place like this unless he's something special to come for. There's absolutely nothing here for an ordinary tourist—' He broke off and shrugged impatiently. 'You don't need me to tell you that.'

He was angry, and yet why should he be? Unless . . . She dared to hope again, but his manner was so repelling that she had no courage to attempt any approach. In any case, what could she say that would not put Clark in the blackest of positions?

'He said that it was my descriptions that had made him decide to come.' This was untrue, as she had not gone into much detail at all about her home here – at least, not to Clark. But Jill hoped this would at least provide some small explanation of the fact of Clark's presence here.

'Don't talk nonsense!' Dean looked contemptuously at her. 'Why don't you come out with the truth?'

Jill's colour faded. She felt she must take refuge in anger, for otherwise she would burst into tears.

'What business is it of yours, anyway? What's the reason for all these questions and sarcastic comments?'

Dean, who had been leaning against the door jamb, straightened up, his expression hard, like stone.

'Forgive me,' he said, but there was really no sign of an apology in the brusque and frigid tone. 'I ought to have learned long ago to mind my own business.'

And a moment later Jill, brushing the ready tears from her lashes, was watching his tall figure disappearing as he went towards the place where he had left his car, under the shade of the clump of tall slender poplars at the side of the house.

CHAPTER NINE

WITH the wattle plantation being started right away Dean was over at Bangali Farm the following afternoon, giving further advice requested by Bob.

'Is anything wrong between you and Dean?' Bob had asked when on informing her that Dean was coming Jill instantly said she would take Jacky and go off for a few hours. This was quite permissible as she had a free day anyway.

'No—' The lie escaped, but Jill coloured. 'Please don't question me, Bob,' she pleaded, and ran from him into the house.

Perhaps, thought Jill, she should have tried to put Bob off. But he and Lucie were bound to realize that a rift had come between her and Dean again. It was impossible that it could escape them.

After getting bathed and changed she asked Lucie's permission if she could have Jacky and, receiving it, she went out to call him from the small paddock in which he grazed. He came slowly towards her and her expression changed. The horse was lame.

'What's wrong, Jacky?' She patted him and he whinneyed. 'Are you in pain?' She went to fetch Bob, and at that moment the low white car rolled along the dusty path. Dean had come earlier than promised and, turning, Jill went back to the house.

'Jacky's lame,' she explained as Lucie stopped what she was doing and sent her a questioning glance. 'I'll go to town instead.'

'Jacky's lame?' repeated Lucie, concerned. 'Is he very bad?'

'I really don't know. I've told Bob – and Dean's just arrived, so he'll probably know what to do.'

'I must go out and see what's wrong,' decided Lucie, wiping her hands on the towel. 'If you're going to town will you take the shopping list with you? Don't make a chore of it, though. Nothing's really urgent, and I shall be going into town myself on Friday.'

Jill changed again, this time into a cotton dress and sandals. As she went out she collected the list from the living-room and a broad-brimmed hat from the hook in the tiny hall.

Dean and Bob turned their heads as the engine of the station wagon caught. Jill lifted a hand as she drove off; Bob responded, but Dean had already turned back to give his attention to Jacky, who was now just outside the paddock. Jill's eyes filled up and for a few seconds she could scarcely see where she was going, but she blinked away the tears and determinedly tried to think of something other than the slight she had just received.

But it didn't help when she was driving past the road leading up to Dean's house, or when, at the top of the rise, she was able to glance down to the grove of tamarisk trees that lay just outside the boundary of the gardens of Nyala Mount. These trees shielded the house from the road, and from the eyes of people using it, but for Jill the picture of house and attractive setting was clearly outlined in her mind. She thought of the empty room Dean had promised her, where she could store some of her furniture if she wished, and she experienced only further dejection as she decided that, as things now were between her and Dean, she would be quite unable to avail herself of his offer.

On reaching town she wondered whether or not to phone Patrick. On the one hand she had no desire for her own company, but on the other she was experiencing the kind of mood that could quite easily develop into impatience should Patrick become too frivolous, or act in some other manner that could result in an aggravation of her mood. In the end she decided not to phone him and after leaving the car on the park she proceeded towards the shops.

She had scarcely entered the bookshop when she was hailed by a masculine voice which brought an instant frown to her forehead. She turned, unsmiling, and faced the man responsible for her present unhappiness. To her surprise he appeared cheerful to the point of elation.

'Jill – how very nice to bump into you like this! I hope you have time to take coffee with me?'

'I don't know . . .'

'Please do. I've something to tell you!'

'Some news about Sylvia?' Had he won her back already? she wondered.

'Yes. But come along and let's have that coffee.' He indicated a nearby café, and after another moment's hesitation she fell into step beside him and they walked to the café.

'You've seen Sylvia?' she asked when they were seated and the order given to the native girl who had approached their table.

'I went to the Springbok Club for a drink,' he explained, going on to say that he made himself inconspicuous behind some potted palms, just in case Sylvia should come, which she did, accompanied by the Drakes and her uncle. 'She looked more desirable than ever,' he resumed, gazing soulfully into space. 'I knew I'd never let her go without a fight.'

'You went to her?' inquired Jill when he lapsed into a thoughtful silence.

'No, certainly not. I wouldn't embarrass her, or put her in a position where she would be caught off her guard.'

'That was thoughtful of you,' with an edge of sarcasm that caused him to cast her a questioning glance, in reply to which nothing would have afforded her greater satisfaction than to remind him of his utter lack of such consideration in her own case, when they were confronted by Dean. However, as good manners forbade such outspokenness she maintained a silence and Clark continued by telling her that eventually Sylvia had spotted him.

'She gave a great start, I can tell you! She looked as if she'd seen a ghost!'

'Which is understandable,' commented Jill smoothly.

'I suppose so.' He glanced up as the waitress appeared with the coffee. He seemed at a loss for words, and Jill had the impression that he was doubtful as to how what he had to say would be received. However, he spoke at last, although his avoidance of her eyes was very noticeable. 'I suddenly got an idea, and slipped out to the garden, surmising she would follow, which she did almost immediately.' Clark stopped again and on

Jill's wide brow a frown gathered. What was he about to impart that caused him to hesitate like this? Inexplicably she knew a tinge of foreboding.

'This idea,' she prompted when he continued to hesitate, 'what was it?'

He coloured slightly, but despite this his mouth was set in an aggressive line.

'I mentioned to you that I wanted to make her jealous – in fact, it seemed to me that this was the only way to treat her, because I know from old that she hated to see me pay any attention to another girl.' He paused; Jill said, her face pale and her eyes narrowed,

'Go on.'

'I reckoned that if I could succeed in making her jealous I was more than half-way to getting her back.'

'So?' Mechanically Jill reached for the sugar and put a spoonful into her coffee.

'I hope you'll try to be understanding – to appreciate my feelings, my desperation to get her back?' Jill said nothing, merely fixing his gaze intently. 'I told her – I told her . . .' He tailed off, gave a little cough to clear his throat and then, apparently aware that the story would have to be told, he began speaking again, avoiding Jill's accusing and disbelieving eyes but adopting a defensive tone for all that. She gasped when at length he stopped, and the cup she had raised to her lips was replaced on its saucer with such force that the contents spilled over on to the tablecloth.

'You actually used me!' For a moment Jill was unable to articulate further words, so choked was she by anger. 'You used me, without my knowledge or consent?' She was still staggered by his effrontery; even now he was displaying not the slightest sign of remorse. 'I just can't take it in!'

'Please try to understand. When she came out to me in the garden of the club it was plain that she'd concluded I'd come over here to find her—'

'It was a very natural conclusion, and a correct one, seeing that you'd explained just how you came to hear of her whereabouts – that you'd learned from me that she had come to stay with the Drakes.'

'True, it was a natural conclusion, and a correct one, as you say. But she was so arrogant and off-hand with me that I wasted no time at all using my idea. As I've just told you, I informed her that although it had been for her that I'd come in the first place, I was now very near to falling in love with you. It worked, Jill,' he added urgently as she would have broken in with some furious remark. 'It worked! She tried to hide her feelings, but I could see she was seething with jealousy underneath.' His eyes lighted up at his own secret thoughts, and once again Jill gasped. His love for Sylvia quite plainly overshadowed everything, including his sense of honour. He was totally uncaring that he had caused Jill distress; all that concerned him was his own happiness, and it would appear that he was quite willing to disregard the feelings of others so long as his own desires could be realized. 'I know you're angry,' he went on, glancing at her white face, 'but do please try to understand how I felt. I had to act in the only way which I knew would be effective. I succeeded in arousing jealousy in her, and I know for sure it's only a matter of time before she comes running to ask my forgiveness.'

Jill looked at him with contempt, and a long moment

passed before, rising to her feet and taking up her hand-bag, she told him frigidly that she was leaving.

'You needn't come with me,' she snapped. 'I don't ever want to speak to you again—'

'I haven't harmed you,' he cut in defensively.

'You have a most strange way of thinking,' she told him coldly. But she would go no further than this; her dignity kept her aloof from argument, or even discussion.

'Have you considered your own position?' he began as she left the table. 'When I win Sylvia back Dean Lester will be left free—' He broke off, for Jill had gone and he was talking to himself.

She had caught his words nevertheless, and she repeated them as she walked back to the place where she had parked the station wagon.

Dean Lester will be left free . . . There was no reason to hope that he would then turn to her, Jill. And in any case, she had no desire to be wanted as second best.

It was on a lonely stretch of road that she first became aware of a strange sound coming from beneath the bonnet; she carried on, her first thought being that, were she to stop, she would not know what to do anyway. Also, the vehicle might not start again if she stopped the engine. But the unfamiliar noise became louder; it was as if something were loose and banging against something else. What must she do? To carry on must surely be damaging to the engine, yet to stop on this lonely road was something she felt loath to do. The open veld stretched away on both sides – towards the mountains in one direction and towards the scattered line of low hills on the other. It all seemed so isolated, though someone would come along eventually, of course. However, the choice was soon out of her hands; the vehicle jerked and the engine spluttered. Managing to steer on to the side of the road before it stopped altogether, she got out. Instinctively she lifted the bonnet, then stared helplessly at what was underneath it. There was nothing to indicate what was wrong, but even had there been some piece of mechanism sticking up anywhere she would not have known what to do with it.

After standing around for a few minutes she got back into the station wagon and waited for someone to come along. Half an hour passed, and then another. She had begun to consider walking back to town when with a great sigh of relief she heard a car approaching from the direction in which she had been proceeding when the station wagon broke down. But her relief turned to a sort of grim dismay when she saw the low white car appear from over the rise ahead. It would have to be Dean! Of all the humiliating positions in which she had found herself this was the worst, she told herself, the colour already mounting her cheeks. The car slid smoothly to a halt in front of hers; Dean's long body emerged and straightened up to its incredible height. Biting her lip with vexation, Jill slid out and looked up into his bronzed face, and because she just had to say something she told him unnecessarily that the station wagon had broken down.

The deep-set grey eyes flickered, hard as steel.

'Obviously it's broken down,' he observed with faint sarcasm. 'I didn't conclude that you were sitting around merely to enjoy the scenery.'

Her colour deepened; she said quietly,

'The engine made a funny noise for about three or four minutes before it stopped altogether.'

'What sort of a noise?' He was opening the bonnet and fixing the support.

'A rattling noise.' She paused. 'It was good of you to stop,' she added awkwardly, and at that he ceased what he was doing for a moment to cast her a look of asperity.

'If you can't think of anything sensible to say, then keep quiet! Anyone would have stopped!'

Jill averted her head, aware of the stupidity of her remark. His manner hurt intolerably – the impatience added to the calm indifference. It was what would have hurt at any time, but just now, when she was still upset by the information imparted by Clark, she felt the sting of Dean's off-handedness so acutely that she could have wept.

She turned aside, but watched him covertly as he touched leads and wires, moving them about. Then he removed a cap of some sort, and put it back. Straightening up at last, he shook his head.

'It's nothing I can repair on the spot,' he stated. 'I think the simplest thing is for me to tow it back into Breysburg and leave it at the garage. If I take you home and Bob telephones to the garage they're going to charge for taking it in. Also, they might not be able to arrange for a tow immediately and we don't want the car left here too long.'

'You mean – I have to steer it while you tow it?'

Dean frowned at her expression.

'There's nothing to it,' he told her abruptly.

'No . . .? I haven't ever done it before.'

Ignoring this, Dean took a tow-rope from the boot of his car and fixed it to a bracket above the bumper. Then he told Jill to get into the station wagon and steer it so that it was turned round. He pushed it with ease from the side of the road and although her heart was beating rapidly, for she was sure she would make a mistake, Jill followed his instructions and soon the station wagon was hitched to the powerful car in front.

He came to her and, standing by the open window, gave her further instructions, telling her when to apply her brakes and emphasizing that they must be applied gently.

'Have you got that?' he asked finally.

She nodded.

'Yes—' She stopped, but just had to add, 'Thank you, Dean—' But he was gone, sliding into his car, and Jill swallowed the painful little lump that had risen in her throat.

All went well for about four or five miles and then, as a little furry animal scurried across the road between the two vehicles, Jill instinctively jammed on her brakes. The rope snapped and Jill's heart jerked, its beats increasing as, having stopped, Dean came from his car, an expression of frowning inquiry on his face.

'What—?'

'I'm so sorry,' she interrupted hastily. 'Something ran across and I didn't want to run over it.'

Silence. Dean's chest rose and fell as he took a deep breath. It was not difficult to see that he was having difficulty with his temper, and with a fleeting glimpse of insight Jill could quite easily visualize the scene were it enacted between Dean and a woman who happened to be his wife. Undoubtedly the lash of his tongue would have descended upon her for forgetting his instructions. She began to make another apology, but once again was left talking to herself. Dean was striding to his car, which was then backed up and a knot tied in the rope.

Without a word he got in and the journey was resumed, this time uneventfully. Town was reached and the station wagon left at the garage, Dean giving instructions that no repairs must be done until the owner had given the order. He used the telephone to inform Bob of what had happened, then told the garage proprietor that Mr. Sharman would be telephoning him within the next few minutes.

Jill was sitting in Dean's car and on noticing him glance at his watch as he slid behind the wheel, she asked anxiously,

'Were you on your way to keep an appointment?'

He nodded, his eyes on the road as he brought the car from the forecourt of the garage.

'I have a luncheon date with Miss de Courcy.'

Silence filled the car; Jill swallowed hard, sitting forward on the edge of her seat.

'I'm so sorry,' she began. 'I've made you late?'

'Not too late.' A sideways glance was cast at her. 'You'll have to join us—'

'No, that isn't necessary,' she cut in, the idea of lunching with Dean and Sylvia having no attractions whatsoever. 'I wouldn't intrude, anyway. If you'll drop me somewhere . . . here—'

'Is that what you prefer?' stiffly and with an edge to

his voice.

'Yes.' She looked at his stern set profile and her mouth quivered. 'Yes, it is what I prefer.'

'Very well.' Finding a suitable place, he brought the car to a standstill and Jill got out. 'I'll be back here at three o'clock,' he informed her, and as she stepped back he let in the clutch and the car moved quietly forward, leaving her standing there, her eyes misted, her lips quivering tremulously.

At last she turned and took a side road leading to the park. But the thought of isolation was unattractive and she preferred the shops. It was a mistake, for the club was at the end and there was the car again, swinging off the road into the palm-bordered drive of the club.

'Jill – again!' exclaimed Clark, coming up to her.

She turned, frowning, and wishing more than ever that she had chosen the park.

'What do you want?' she asked shortly. 'I told you I never wanted to speak to you again.'

'Don't be like this,' he pleaded. 'What's happened. anyway? I imagined you were intending to go home after you left me.'

'The car broke down.'

'It did? Where is it now?' He seemed completely at his ease, she noticed with disgust. He was cheerful too, and she could not help wondering what would be his reaction were she to tell him that Sylvia was lunching at the Springbok Hotel with Dean. 'Whereabouts were you when it broke down?'

She hesitated, then told him. He wanted to know more, but she merely said she'd managed to get a tow back to town and that the station wagon was now in a garage. Clark then asked how she was to get back home.

'I'll get a lift,' she replied, so abruptly that he was deterred from questioning her further. He didn't even ask what time her lift was, but he did invite her to join him for lunch.

'I thought of the Grand,' he added. 'I lunched there the day after my arrival.'

'I don't know—'

'Go on,' he interrupted persuasively. 'Let's eat together and forget our differences.'

Jill stood there, irresolute, amazing herself by remaining with Clark when her instinct was to walk away from him. But so deep was her dejection that any company seemed better than none, the time from now till three o'clock being an eternity, with the picture of Dean and Sylvia lunching together occupying her mind to such an extent that nothing else could intrude.

'Very well,' she agreed at last. 'I'll come with you.' She was fully aware that her acceptance was spoken in a far from gracious manner, but she was not feeling any better disposed towards Clark than she was earlier in the day.

The bar of the Grand was an intimate place, overhung with palms in pots and exotic flowers growing from rockeries circling out from the corners of the room.

Jill and Clark sat down and their drink was brought to them. They were given the menu and as there was only one they had to sit close in order to peruse it. And it was while they were thus engaged that Clark gave a small exclamation and Jill glanced up to see Dean and his lovely companion entering the bar, obviously having, for some reason, changed their minds about lunching at the club. Jill's heart caught, and colour leapt to her cheeks as her eyes met those of Dean. He stared, disbelievingly at first, but then his eyes hardened to points of steel and flickered from her to the man at her side. Meanwhile, Sylvia, looking like something out of a boutique window, set her mouth petulantly as she looked at Clark.

'They're coming over,' faltered Jill, feeling that the fates indeed were against her.

But all they did was to pass by on their way to a table farther along the room. As they came abreast of them Dean inclined his head in a cool little gesture and Sylvia merely turned her head the other way.

CHAPTER TEN

GETTING ready for the barbecue was an ordeal to Jill; she wavered several times, wondering if she dared tell Bob that she was not going. But that would only result in Bob and Lucie being put in an awkward position, so Jill resignedly decided she must attend.

She wore a white shirt and red slacks, and a band on her hair tied in a small bow against her temple. She had no wish that her hair should appear untidy at the first breathing of the wind upon it.

They drove over to Nyala Mount in the station wagon, which had been very promptly repaired and delivered to Bangali Farm. It was now good for at least a year, pronounced Bob, who added that by the end of that time he hoped to be able to afford something a little better.

Dean was with a group of people including Sylvia and her uncle, but he instantly excused himself in order that he might come over to greet the new arrivals. His grey eyes, narrowed so that their expression was masked, rested on Jill's face before flickering over her slender figure. She flushed a little under this unreadable scrutiny and then glanced at Sylvia. She was clad in a glamorous trouser suit of vivid green, with a black sweater coming high in the neck. She scintillated, having come – so it seemed to Jill – straight from a beauty salon.

Deprecatingly Jill glanced down at her own attire, which, until she had seen Sylvia, had in her opinion been so right for the *braaivleis* where everyone would be walking about under the stars, informally eating sausages and steaks from disposable plates.

'So you decided to come?' The whisper, made close to Jill's ear as both Bob and Lucie turned away on being addressed by Charles Goulding, was half statement, half question, and voiced in tones of sardonic amusement, although no trace of humour softened the eyes or mouth. 'What amount of emotional discomfort did you endure before reaching your decision?'

Her eyes glinted. Nevertheless, this perception took her aback a little and the colour in her cheeks increased.

'You're very clever, aren't you?'

The grey eyes opened. A faint curve of the lips was the shadow of a smile. How superior he was! Jill knew a total return of her original opinion of him.

'Can't you think of anything a little less trite than that?' he said suavely. 'Or have I disconcerted you so greatly that you can't think as clearly as you usually do?'

Her small chin went up; the breeze tousled her hair and despite the ribbon a lock fell out of place and moved against her temple. Dean's eyes seemed to dart towards Sylvia, whose heavily-lacquered coiffure remained immaculate. The sense of her own imperfections seemed to swell to such proportions that a feeling of actual inferiority swept through Jill. She hated her clothes – without even taking the glance around that would have shown almost every other woman similarly attired; she was conscious of her unruly fringe, of her lack of make-up, and even her slim brown hands seemed to cause her some embarrassment. And because of this unhappy sensation of inadequacy, anger and indignation rose as a defence and, forgetting that she was a guest on whom it was incumbent to display politeness and tact, she retorted arrogantly,

'I expect I'm trite because I'm not very smart in dealing with people like you! Perhaps you'd be happier if you returned to your more sophisticated companion!' The colour had receded a little from her cheeks; she was looking up at Dean's face through a sudden mist and she had to blink rapidly to remove it. Her raised voice had quite naturally attracted the attention of her brother and sister-in-law and they turned their heads. As Charles went off they were free to give their whole attention to the two standing there, and both Lucie and her husband sent inquiring glances from Dean to Jill before Bob said cautiously,

'Something wrong?'

Dean was slanting Jill a satirical look, his mouth slowly curving into a faint smile. Amusement, rather than anger, was evident in his eyes; he appeared to be deriving a great measure of satisfaction from her embarrassment, and even decided to add to it by saying, in a bantering tone,

'Not really, Bob. Jill's in one of her moods, that's all. Were I her brother I'd put her across my knee.'

A silence followed, then Lucie gave a light laugh. But Jill had coloured hotly, and her fists clenched at her sides. Of a surety it was *she* who would have struck *him* had they been alone!

Bob was experiencing a degree of awkwardness and, taking his wife's arm, he said,

'I see someone over there that I want to talk to. Come along, dear.'

A low laugh escaped Dean immediately they were out of earshot.

'You didn't get down to answering my question,' he said presently, and she looked up.

'Question?' she repeated, her tones ice-edged.

'I asked how long it took you to reach the final decision to accept my invitation.'

'I accepted it when you gave it.'

'And changed your mind several times afterwards.'

Jill fumbled for words. Dean gave another low laugh.

'All right,' she admitted, seeing that there was little else she could do than be wholly honest with him, 'I did have moments of indecision.'

'Because?'

Glancing over to where Sylvia was standing with the Drakes, her uncle, and several others including Wally and Patrick, Jill said,

'Your friend's looking this way. I wouldn't wish to keep you from her.'

Dean's deep-set eyes narrowed but were not in any way hard. In fact, his whole manner was strange, she thought, on dwelling on it for a second or two. There was mockery and sarcasm, and the clear intention of reducing her to the very depths of embarrassment, but no real hostility was apparent in his attitude towards her.

'I shall join my friend when it suits me to do so,' he informed Jill smoothly. 'Meanwhile, I'll have no more prevarication on your part. Why did you have moments of indecision?' And, when she merely frowned and made no attempt to answer, 'If it's diplomacy that's deterring you then I'd like to remind you that it's a little late for it now.' A small pause. 'Don't you agree?'

Jill's teeth set. She glared at him and said that if he had quite finished trying to embarrass her she would like to excuse herself and join her friend.

'Your friend? I wasn't aware I'd invited *him* here tonight.'

'I meant Patrick,' she returned frigidly.

'Ah, Patrick . . . the other boy-friend. But I assumed you'd thrown him over for – er–' He shook his head. 'What was the fellow's name?'

She glanced suspiciously at him.

'I can't think you're the kind of man to forget names,' she said quietly. And then, before she could even guess what he had in mind, she was taken roughly by the arm and propelled away from the lights, into the seclusion and dimness of the woodland beyond the lawn.

'Now,' he said evenly, 'you'll tell me why you had these moments of indecision?'

She stared at him, even while she endeavoured, quite futilely, to extricate herself from the rather painful grip he had upon her arms.

'I don't understand you–' She broke off as he shook her. '*Don't!*' she flared, but he took not the slightest notice, merely tightening his grip as she twisted angrily in her attempt to escape.

'Answer me!'

She caught her underlip between her teeth as the tears sprang to her eyes. Bewildered she most certainly was by his manner, but so great was her unhappiness that it overshadowed any thought of an analysis of his behaviour. Had she been able to divert her mind sufficiently she would have seen the obvious: that there must be some logical reason for the attitude of the man whose normal mien was one of unemotional urbanity. He was even now giving her another shake and repeating his command.

'All right,' she cried, 'I will answer you! I had misgivings about coming tonight owing to the way you've been with me lately. Your antagonism's returned – and increased, and you know very well that you only extended the invitation to me because you were forced to do so! I kn-knew you didn't really want m-me, and that's why I was so – so undecided.' A hand was brushed swiftly across her eyes, and she averted her head. Never would she give him the satisfaction of knowing that he held the power to make her cry.

'My antagonism's returned, has it?' Releasing her, he kept his eyes fixed on her bent head. 'And I didn't really want you here tonight?'

'I'm fully aware that you didn't.' She raised her head, as if forced to do so by his insistent stare. 'The only person you're interested in is . . .' Jill's voice faded as the girl she was about to mention appeared suddenly out of the darkness of the trees. She must have circled round in order to make her approach from this direction, thought Jill, and wondered how much she had heard.

'Oh, there you are!' she exclaimed brightly. 'I've been looking all over for you, Dean.' Sylvia's eyes flickered to Jill. 'I do hope I haven't interrupted anything? I just wanted to find Dean.'

'Well,' returned Jill with what could only be described as acid sweetness, 'you've found him.' And with that she turned and walked away, her head in the air.

Patrick came to her immediately she advanced on to the lighted lawn and together they went over to the charcoal stove and helped themselves to the delicious chops and other meats being cooked there.

'Let's sit here, under this tree. I say,' went on Patrick when they were seated, 'what's all this about you and a fellow named Clark? It's all over town that he's fallen for you.'

She set her teeth.

'He spread it around. It isn't true.'

'It isn't true? He says he's in love with you. He met you in England when you were over – is that right?'

'I did meet him, yes. But there's nothing in the rumour that—'

'Rumour?' with a slight lift of his brows. 'You've been going around with him, you'll admit that?'

'I've dined with him once, and lunched with him once,' she said with some asperity. 'You can hardly call that going around with him.'

Patrick shrugged, but it was plain that he still believed what he had heard. However, he made no further comment and a silence fell between them. Jill's thoughts dismally concentrated on this rumour about which everyone was curious.

However, she was not to dwell on it for long, as Bob and Lucie and several others came up and joined her and Patrick and the conversation became light and general. Dean and Sylvia could be seen, but they were not alone. Sylvia's uncle and the Drakes were with them.

After a while a band of musicians, five in number,

173

began to play and several couples went on to the stoep to dance, among them Dean and Sylvia, a striking pair who moved in perfect harmony, so that they attracted the attention of all those who were not themselves dancing.

'Gosh, but she's a real beauty!' Patrick was making this exclamation even while he was rising and holding out a hand to Jill, silently inviting her to dance. They went over to join the others on the stoep and she slipped into Patrick's arms. An odd sort of smile lifted the corners of Dean's mouth as he caught her eye; she turned her head the other way. What an interminable evening! Would it never come to an end? Never again would she accept an invitation of Dean's; this was definitely her last visit to Nyala Mount. A sigh of nostalgia escaped her at the memory of the happy times she had spent here in the days when it was owned by the Fenwicks. Had they never left then she and Dean would never have met. So much for the workings of fate, which ordained that their paths must cross and her whole life be upset. Jill felt she would have traded ten years of that life for a return to the days when her heart was free from this weight of dejection that seemed always to be present now, marring her appreciation of the lovely country in which she lived and had grown so much to love.

Her thoughts naturally strayed to the possibility of a marriage between Dean and Sylvia and she knew without a trace of doubt that if this did occur then she must leave Africa for ever.

Clark's face intruded; she recalled his optimism, which seemed utterly absurd at this moment when

Sylvia, dancing close to Dean, was looking up into his handsome face and clearly flirting with him. The rumour Clark had set in motion was worthless, Jill decided. There was not the least sign that Sylvia cared for any man other than the one with whom she was dancing.

The music stopped eventually and the couples came down from the stoep on to the lawn; they strolled about or stood in groups. Some began eating again while others lingered at the long table where the wine scintillated richly in the light from the lanterns in the trees above.

It was a balmy African night with a full moon spraying the gardens and lawn and the silent drowsy bushveld. Jill wandered away by herself, desiring only to be alone for a while. But this solitude was denied her and she frowned as she turned to discover whose footsteps were intruding into her silence. Sylvia!

'Ah, Miss Sharman,' she purred, coming abreast of her. 'I've wanted to have a few words with you and now here's my opportunity. I followed you—' She glanced around. 'Can we sit over there, by that delightful bougainvillaea hedge? I do so adore Dean's garden! It's full of the most lovely surprises! Imagine finding a pretty little stone seat in this secluded spot!'

'What exactly do you want?' inquired Jill coldly, taken aback by Syvia's presence, and her request.

'It's about you and Clark,' she began, and Jill waited with interest through the small pause which followed. 'He tells me he's in love with you. Is this true?'

Jill became guarded, vividly recalling the occasion when Sylvia twisted her words when repeating to Dean what she had said.

'I'm not quite sure what you're trying to establish?' she parried.

'You, Miss Sharman? How do you feel about Clark?'

'Your fiancé? How should I feel about him?'

The girl's eyes glittered, glassy and brittle.

'He's not my fiancé!'

'He gave me to understand he was. The reason he came over here was to try to effect a reconciliation.'

'What right had you to talk about me? He'd never have found me if it hadn't been for you!' Sylvia sat down, but Jill remained standing.

'I didn't talk about you – not deliberately. Your name was mentioned, as the fiancée of Clark, and I said that there was a girl of that name here. It was an unusual name, and you were obviously the girl who had run away from Clark—'

'You had no right to give Clark my address here!'

'Can I ask you a question?' said Jill, ignoring this. And, when Sylvia nodded absently, 'Have you finished altogether with Clark?'

'Most certainly I have!'

'He believes you'll go back to him.'

'Then he's crazy! What girl would look at him when she can have a man like Dean?' The eyes became steady, fixing Jill's face in the moonlight. 'I can have Dean, you know, Miss Sharman, so you might as well give up. Oh, yes, I heard your clever little stammering efforts earlier when I intruded into your conversation with him. But you yourself were about to admit that you were fully aware that it was me he's interested in, weren't you?'

'You listened?' Jill's gaze swept her contemptuously.

'You're despicable!'

The girl laughed, gratingly.

'You're in love with Dean. But, Miss Sharman, why don't you take what's more available? You could have Clark without much trouble.'

Again Jill's eyes swept her contemptuously.

'If you have nothing more to say, Miss de Courcy,' she said, 'I'll leave you.'

'I have plenty more to say.' A pause and then, in slow invidious tones, 'Dean happens to be mine . . . don't you forget it, Miss Sharman. How you could ever even have conceived the idea that he would be interested in a little dowd like you amazes me. Take my advice: have Clark while the opportunity's there. You're not in the first flush of youth from what I can see, and also here in this outlandish part of the world there's the possibility that you'll never have another opportunity—' Sylvia broke off. Jill was already becoming a mere shadow in the dimness of the trees under which she was angrily striding out.

It was a couple of hours later that, with everyone drifting away, Jill stood with her brother and Lucie watching Dean saying goodnight to his guests. The cars and other vehicles passed one by one along the drive, their rear lights forming a double line until, with the disappearance of the final car, the drive was once more bathed in shade.

'I expect we should also be moving,' from Jill who, had the decision been hers, would have been among the very first to leave.

Sylvia had returned soon after she herself had rejoined the party, and had scarcely left Dean's side for the rest of the evening. Dean had often seemed deliberately to seek Jill's eye, but as all she caught was an expression of mockery or amusement she instantly turned her head away. He had danced with her a couple of times, but although the hostility was definitely lacking in his manner all that replaced it was an air that seemed very close to boredom. Yet Jill had been puzzled; she had felt that, hovering just a little way out of reach, was some momentous revelation, but so impatient did she become with her inability to understand this strange new manner of Dean's that she forced herself to concentrate on something less frustrating.

She thought of Clark, and his hopes and optimism; these were soon to be shattered, for even should nothing come of the affair between Sylvia and Dean, it was most unlikely that she would turn again to the man who, in his own opinion, was still her fiancé. As for Sylvia's advice to Jill that she herself should aim at winning Clark – the reason for this was plain. With Jill and Clark engaged then she, Sylvia, would be sure she was safe from exposure by either of them.

Bob was saying yes, they ought to be moving; he was looking oddly at his wife, Jill noticed in some surprise. Lucie in turn glanced – almost surreptitiously – at Jill, then turned her head away. What was the matter with them? wondered Jill with a frown.

Dean returned, walking majestically across the paved courtyard that lay to one side of the house, the side where all the vehicles had been parked.

He stood looking down at Jill; Bob and Lucie stared and smiled faintly.

'I've something to show you, Jill.' Dean did no more than take her arm, and although she protested by reminding him of the lateness of the hour, he had her inside the house almost before she knew it.

'Bob and Lucie,' she began, turning her head. 'Aren't they coming—?'

'No, my dear Jill. They're *going*.' So calm the voice as this staggering information was given. Jill gave a start and would instinctively have run back on to the stoep, but her wrist was firmly held. She heard the heavy rattle of the engine as it was revved up. Her eyes were lifted questioningly – and a little fearfully – to Dean's dark unsmiling countenance.

'What's going on?' she demanded. 'They've left me behind!'

'A clever observation, my dear. Yes, they've left you behind – at my request—'

'But—'

'You're quite safe.' A sardonic edge to his voice and lips that curved upwards at the corners in a smile of amusement. But it was Dean's eyes that held her – held her like a magnet. For in them was an expression she had never encountered before. 'Your brother would hardly have left you here had he not been convinced that my intentions were honourable.'

She stared at him, blank-faced, even while her heart was throbbing with a wild joy and her whole mind and body seemed to be uplifted. Yet in this moment her thoughts darted absurdly to her unruly hair and she put a hand to it. The ribbon caught in her fingers and came away; she gazed at it in dismay and suddenly Dean laughed, a low but vibrant laugh, and he took the ribbon from her trembling fingers and laid it aside on a chair.

'Why – why has Bob l-left me?' she managed to ask, though in tones no louder than a whisper.

'So that you and I can sort things out— Oh, yes, I know tomorrow would have done well enough, but I'm fast reaching the point where my patience cannot be contained any longer. Don't look so alarmed, child,' he added with a frown, 'I shall take you back to Bangali Farm later.'

'They'll have gone to bed,' she murmured, feeling extremely foolish at her inability to find something more eloquent to say at a time like this, when her heart was bounding and her pulse throbbed as there swept through her an almost uncontrollable yearning for the feel of Dean's arms about her.

'Undoubtedly. Bob promised to leave the front door unlocked.'

'Why – why is Bob in this?' Her body quivered, in sympathy with the unruly thoughts that flitted about in her mind, bewildered thoughts, and yet through them had already emerged the conviction that Dean cared for her. How could it be otherwise when he was looking at her like this? 'You didn't have anything to show me, did you?' she asked absurdly, and his lips twitched in amusement.

'You have a great deal to thank Bob for,' he said, pausing a moment as she darted him a look of perplexed interrogation. 'He thought it was high time he came out with the secret—'

'The secret?'

'Clark,' he said briefly, and for an instant the grey eyes were as coldly metallic as Jill had ever seen them.

'You mean – Bob told you why Clark came out here?'

'Exactly!'

'I told him it had to be kept a secret . . .' Her voice faltered and she swallowed convulsively, for it did seem that a great surge of anger had taken possession of Dean.

'You explained the whole situation to Bob,' said Dean grittingly, 'but when I asked you for an explanation you lost your temper and told me to mind my own business!'

'No, Dean,' she denied hastily. 'I didn't tell you to mind your own business – not exactly.'

The grey eyes glinted; there was nothing loverlike in their expression now.

'If you begin splitting hairs again,' he threatened in a very soft voice, 'I'll give you what I've itched to give you for a very long time. You're at my mercy, remember.' And as if to illustrate this a little clearer he closed the door leading to the stoep and drew the curtains together, shutting out the warm moonlit night. He began to talk, admonishing her for allowing Clark to spread that rumour, and for shielding him in the first place.

'I was sorry for him,' she protested in defence of her behaviour.

'For him – but not for me!'

She instinctively lifted her chin at this, and for a moment she felt she was back at that sparring stage that had characterized their relationship at the beginning.

'You didn't need pity! You were thoroughly enjoying yourself with Sylvia!'

A small silence ensued, with Jill colouring at the

knowledge of her revealing her jealousy, and Dean deriving considerable amusement from her embarrassment, as he had derived amusement earlier in the evening.

'Her attitude was a most pleasant contrast to that of yours,' he responded smoothly. 'Her manners too were rather better. She was never so rude as to tell me I was conceited and filled with a sense of my own superiority.'

Jill's colour heightened.

'But then,' she retorted cuttingly, 'I don't expect you ever called her bitchy – which you did with me!'

'I spoke only the truth.'

'In that case,' she quivered you'd better take me home! For I'm sure you don't want—' She got no further as, with total disregard for gentleness, Dean jerked her towards him, with a grip on her wrist that caused her to wince, and his lips came down on hers in a kiss that held everything except tenderness – it was savage, possessive, masterful all in one.

'I didn't keep you here so that we could have a fight,' he told her when at last he took his mouth from hers. 'We can fight to our hearts' content when we're married!'

'Married . . .' The brown eyes shone up at him despite the hardness displayed in his. 'Dean, do you really mean it?'

He looked at her, and slowly his expression changed and his eyes and mouth became tender. She invited another kiss in spite of the fact that her mouth still hurt from its previous contact with his.

'You know very well I mean it,' he told her with a

little shake of his head that was a censorious gesture. 'You and I were meant to get together, and had it been left to me we'd have been married within a month of your coming out here.'

'Dean . . .' She gave him a tender, apologetic look. 'I wish I'd known. Bob told me you'd said I was – was – nice.'

Amusement curved his lips.

'I said rather more than that, if I remember correctly. However, it's of no matter now.' A pause and then, 'Why, when Bob had told you this, didn't you realize at once that I loved you?'

'I expect it was because I felt that a man like you would never fall in love so quickly,' she said after some thought. 'And later, after the arrival of Sylvia, I thought you would probably fall in love with her.'

He shook his head, slanting her an impatient glance.

'Can you honestly see me with a shallow type like that?' Jill made no answer, but merely shook her head in an abstracted sort of way, for the only really important thing with her at present was that she was in Dean's arms and her head resting against his breast, in the most comfortable and enjoyable way possible. 'There's so much to explain, my love,' he was saying, his lips close to her hair, 'but it can be left for the time being.' And with gentle tender fingers he brought her head up and kissed her again. She gave a deep and ecstatic sigh and a low laugh escaped him.

'Dearest Jill,' he murmured, 'I love you.' The last three words, so simply spoken, came out on a note of ardency that thrilled her even before her slender body was brought into the closest intimacy with his. 'I ought to be taking you home,' he whispered, but immediately led her to a couch and, drawing her down with him, he enclosed her in his arms again. And they talked after all, clearing up many misunderstandings without a single fiery word escaping either of them. Dean was still just a little sore at the way Jill had allowed Clark to get away with the lies he had told on that first meeting with Dean, when he had declared that she had invited him over. Jill said, a little contritely,

'Had I known you cared for me I most certainly would never have let you be hurt. As it was, I felt I couldn't expose Clark as a liar.' She waited, but on receiving no response to this she added, this time a little plaintively, 'Clark heard that you'd been going about with Sylvia all the time I was away in England.'

'All the time?' he frowned. 'I took her to dinner one evening, and I met her at a party which Charles gave. I think that's about all. How could he have got the idea that I was with her all the time?'

'I don't know.' It didn't matter anyway, she thought, and allowed the matter to drop. But she did ask after a while, as the thought occurred to her, 'Were you sorry for Sylvia?'

'Of course; every man was.'

'You now know she doesn't need pity, and never did,' Jill couldn't help saying, and Dean laughed and said she was being bitchy again, at which she blushed in so adorable a way that she was swept into an embrace that left her gasping for breath when at length she was released.

'If you consider me bitchy,' she pouted, 'then I don't

know why you want to marry me.'

Dean's eyes lit with amusement.

'For the enjoyment of curing you,' he said. 'I shall take a stick to you every time you come out with a bitchy remark.'

Jill laughed, but shakily, and buried her head in his coat.

'I was so jealous of her,' she murmured huskily at last. 'Even tonight you were with her nearly all the time—' She drew away and looked up into his face. 'When was it that Bob told you about Clark and Sylvia?'

'On the phone this afternoon. He had seen how unhappy you were; he had heard the rumour that Clark had spread around and guessed it was that which was creating a rift between you and me. So he decided to take a hand and disclose everything to me. He said he was pretty sure that you loved me.'

'But if you knew right at the beginning of the evening why did you give her all your attention?'

'I didn't at first,' he reminded Jill, going on to say that immediately on hearing the whole story from Bob he had been impatient to have the disunity between Jill and himself cleared up, hence his taking her away to that secluded spot in the grounds. 'You weren't in the right mood for a love scene,' he continued, his deep-toned voice edged with amusement, 'and in any case we were interrupted. But I kept on trying to catch your eyes, and to convey my feelings. You shunned my attempts, turning your back on me, so I expect it was pique that made me give Sylvia all my attention.'

Jill bit her lip, realizing now that she had asked for all

she had received.

'If it's any consolation to you,' she responded with all honesty, 'I went through misery.'

At this he held her tenderly, and his lips were so very gentle as they touched hers.

'It isn't any consolation to me, my love. All I want is for you to be happy. It's all I shall ever want.'

She smiled and her eyes glowed with the rapture within her.

'Because you know that in loving you I'll be happy,' she said, and his immediate rejoiner was,

'Happy loving me ... and in being loved in return.'

She snuggled close against him, felt his heart beating almost as wildly as her own. Her thoughts darted about; she recalled that when she had tried to convince him that Clark was not her boy-friend he would not listen, and she recalled other incidents that had caused friction between her and Dean. Tomorrow, she decided sleepily, she and Dean would have another long talk, and the last misunderstanding would disappear. But for now she was content to nestle in the protection of his arms, and thrill to the warmth and strength of his hard body against hers.

'Dearest,' he whispered a long while later, his warm lips caressing her lips and her cheek and the smooth curve of her throat, 'it's time I took you home.'

'Must you?' The words were out before she realized what they might be taken to mean and the blood rushed to her face. Dean laughed and said teasingly,

'I feel just the same, my love, but I do think we ought to respect the demands of propriety, especially as your brother trusted me to take you home, once we had resolved our differences.' A pause so that she could comment, but, still flushing with embarrassment, she once again sought the refuge of his coat. But he brought her face from it, and looked tenderly into her eyes. 'In less than a week we'll be married, my Jill. Does that suit you?'

She tried to speak, but something blocked her throat, so she conveyed her agreement with her eyes, which was easy, since they shone with rapture and adoration and all the love she felt for him.

Hand in hand she and Dean came out on to the stoep; high in the velvet African sky shone the moon, and from a long way off came the mystic, primeval pulse of a native drumbeat. Closer too, in the lovely gardens of Nyala Mount, tall palms swayed in the gentle breeze, and the perfume of orange flowers filled the warm balmy air.

'Africa, my home,' breathed Jill silently as, her small hand still clasped tightly in that of her lover, she walked beside him towards the gleaming white car standing by the side of the house.

Mills & Boon's Paperbacks

JULY

THE GREATER HAPPINESS by Katrina Britt

Emmy's small delicate nephew was a great responsibility, and she had firmly decided to keep any ideas of love and marriage in the background for two years until the child's health improved. But when she made that vow she hadn't foreseen going to live in Switzerland and meeting the impressive Duc Breul de Polain et Bouvais!

THE BEADS OF NEMESIS by Elizabeth Hunter

Pericles Holmes had married Morag Grant as a matter of convenience, but she had lost no time in falling in love with him. Whereupon her beautiful sister Delia, who always got everything she wanted, announced that she wanted Pericles!

TOO YOUNG TO MARRY by Rosalind Brett

Lorna was eighteen and inexperienced. She was also alone and with very little money, in the strange world of the South Sea Islands, and how was she to be looked after if not by a husband? So Paul Westbrook married her, meaning to keep his distance until she was older – and found events harder to control than he had expected.

THE ARROGANCE OF LOVE by Anne Mather

Dominic Halstad was the most attractive man Susan had ever met, and made her rather difficult fiancé David seem dull by comparison. But even if her first loyalty were not to David, what right had she to think about Dominic – a married man?

THE HABIT OF LOVE by Joyce Dingwell

Brit had always spoiled and indulged her young sister Cara – so perhaps she deserved it when Cara rewarded her by leaving her without a penny in the world. Link Wayland came to the rescue with the suggestion that she marry him – but was that the answer to Brit's problems?

20p net each

Mills & Boon's Paperbacks

JULY (contd.)

THE HOUSE OF THE EAGLES by Elizabeth Ashton

Lois had tried to make herself believe that her romance with Val Daventry was only a holiday affair – but she knew in her heart that it was much more than that, that she would never love any other man. But unfortunately Val didn't seem to feel the same way . . .

CONNELLY'S CASTLE by Gloria Bevan

Julie had never expected to inherit a property in New Zealand, and when she went there to inspect it she kept quiet about her real identity. And only after she had fallen in love with Scott Connelly did she realize what she had done – for Scott was not a man who would take kindly to being deceived . . .

WEB OF SILVER by Lucy Gillen

Jody was looking forward to her beloved foster-parents' silver wedding party – except for the fact that it meant she would have to meet Ross Drummond again. She had always disliked Ross and he had had no time for her. But perhaps things would have changed since their last meeting. Or again, perhaps they wouldn't . . .

FETTERS OF HATE by Anne Hampson

On their wedding day the formidable Nick Vakotis told Helen, 'Remember always that you're mine. Should another man ever enter your life, then you'll wish with all your heart you'd never been born!' What would happen if he discovered that Helen's real reason for marrying him was to forget Paul, husband of her best friend?

A PROMISE TO KEEP by Dorothy Cork

Lesley's marriage to Guy had to be postponed when she was needed to nurse her grandmother. Now she flew out to join her fiancé in Australia. But there she learned that Jane, her little niece, needed her help. Lesley promised that she would go, but Guy warned her that he wasn't prepared to wait for her for ever. Was Lesley carrying family loyalty too far? What should she do?

20p net each

Mills & Boon's Paperbacks

AUGUST

ACROSS THE LAGOON by Roumelia Lane
A lighthearted love story set in Venice in summer.

NO QUARTER ASKED by Janet Dailey
Rich girl Stacey was trying to sample 'real life'. Why should Cord Harris be so disapproving?

DARK MOONLESS NIGHT by Anne Mather
Caroline had turned Gareth down once. Now they were to meet again. How would each of them feel after so long?

THE TOWER OF THE CAPTIVE by Violet Winspear
Rafael and Vanessa had opposing attitudes towards the amount of freedom women should have. What would happen if they fell in love?

BACHELORS GALORE by Essie Summers
Marty had *not* gone to New Zealand to find a husband. But she was a very attractive girl . . .

THE YELLOW MOON by Rebecca Stratton
How could Catherine bear to hand over her little brothers to a man none of them knew?

STARS OVER SARAWAK by Anne Hampson
In the jungle of Sarawak, Carl had saved Roanna's life – and a tribal saying declared that that life now belonged to him . . .

McCABE'S KINGDOM by Margaret Way
Katia had given up her career to look after her mother – but her stepbrother Thorn was to prove a much bigger problem!

THE PAPER MARRIAGE by Flora Kidd
Brooke and Meredith had married 'on paper only'. Suppose one of the marriage partners fell in love?

SONG CYCLE by Mary Burchell
Would family troubles prevent Anna from succeeding in the musical career on which she had set her heart?

20p net each

MILLS & BOON FIESTA!

25 Favourite Titles Now Available Once Again

MILLS & BOON have brought 25 of their favourite
titles back into print. If you would like to obtain any of
these titles please contact your local stockist or in case of
difficulty please use the order form overleaf for your
requirements, enclosing your remittance.

FREE! Your copy of our magazine of MILLS & BOON
romances

Complete the coupon below and send it to MILLS &
BOON READER SERVICE, P.O. Box 236, 14 Sander-
stead Road, S. Croydon, Surrey CR2 OYG we will
gladly send you, post free, your own copy of our magazine – 'Happy Reading' – together with our complete
stock list of over 400 Mills & Boon romances.

Please send me the free Mills & Boon romance
magazine ☐

Please send me the titles ticked ☐

I enclose £.... (No C.O.D.) Please add 2p per
book for postage (10p outside UK)

Name .... Miss/Mrs

Address ....

City/Town..

County/Country ...... Postal/Zip Code/ ....

DID YOU MISS THESE TITLES?

☐ THE SEA CHANGE	*Catherine Airlie*
☐ LAKE OF SHADOWS	*Jane Arbor*
☐ THE WHITE OLEANDER	*Kathryn Blair*
☐ STORMY HAVEN	*Rosalind Brett*
☐ ACCOMPANIED BY HIS WIFE	*Mary Burchell*
☐ THE HOSPITAL OF FATIMA	*Isobel Chace*
☐ AT THE VILLA MASSINA	*Celine Conway*
☐ THE TIMBER MAN	*Joyce Dingwell*
☐ A CHANGE FOR CLANCY	*Amanda Doyle*
☐ SONG OF SUMMER	*Eleanor Farnes*
☐ DOCTOR IN BRAZIL	*Patricia Fenwick*
☐ SURGERY IN THE HILLS	*Ivy Ferarri*
☐ YOUNG BAR	*Jane Fraser*
☐ APPLE ISLAND	*Gladys Fullbrook*
☐ LOVE FROM A SURGEON	*Elizabeth Gilzean*
☐ CHERRY BLOSSOM CLINIC	*Elizabeth Hunter*
☐ ISLAND IN THE DAWN	*Averil Ives*
☐ THE TAMING OF LAURA	*Rachel Lindsay*
☐ CRANE CASTLE	*Jean S. MacLeod*
☐ NEW DREAMS FOR OLD	*Jane Marnay*
☐ DEAR DRAGON	*Sara Seale*
☐ THE CAPTAIN'S TABLE	*Alex Stuart*
☐ HIS SERENE MISS SMITH	*Essie Summers*
☐ GIRL ABOUT TOWN	*Anne Weale*
☐ THE TURQUOISE SEA	*Hilary Wilde*

All priced at 20p. See over for handy order form.
Please tick titles required